13312

# Oceans

WILDSIDE

Nick Davies

Conserving animals and plants in a changing world

BBC BOOKS

Published by BBC Books,
a division of BBC Enterprises Limited,
Woodlands, 80 Wood Lane, London W12 0TT

First published 1992



ISBN 0 563 36120 4

Designed by Neville Graham

Printed in Great Britain by
Butler & Tanner Ltd, Frome and London

# Contents


Nations of the sea . . . . . . . . . . . . 4
Planet Ocean . . . . . . . . . . . . . . . 6
Poisons in the sea . . . . . . . . . . . . 8
Blue water... . . . . . . . . . . . . . 10
...Black death . . . . . . . . . . . . . 12
On the rocks . . . . . . . . . . . . . . . 14
The silver strand . . . . . . . . . . . 16
Beside the seaside . . . . . . . . . . 18
Where rivers meet the sea . . . 20
The seal scare . . . . . . . . . . . . . 22
Seabirds ashore . . . . . . . . . . . . 24
Otters, urchins and abalones 26
Paddling trees . . . . . . . . . . . . . 28
Sea meadows and sea cows . . . 30
Green fields in the water . . . . . 32
Inland sea . . . . . . . . . . . . . . . . . 34
Forests of coral . . . . . . . . . . . . . 36
Raiders of the reef . . . . . . . . . . 38
Treasure islands . . . . . . . . . . . 40
Ocean wanderers . . . . . . . . . . . 42
Fishing for trouble . . . . . . . . . . 44
Wall of death . . . . . . . . . . . . . . . 46
Shark! . . . . . . . . . . . . . . . . . . . . 48
The deepest ocean . . . . . . . . . . 50
Sea of ice . . . . . . . . . . . . . . . . . . 52
The coldest restaurant on Earth . . . . . . . . . . . . . . . . 54
Captive killers . . . . . . . . . . . . . 56
A terrible slaughter . . . . . . . . . 58
The killing goes on . . . . . . . . . . 60
Save our seas! . . . . . . . . . . . . . 62
Useful addresses . . . . . . . . . . . 63
Index . . . . . . . . . . . . . . . . . . . . . 64


## About this book

LIFE ON EARTH began in the sea 600 million years ago – 200 million years before the first land-animals evolved. Because we ourselves live on the land, we tend to forget the long ancestry of marine life and to regard the sea as a salty soup whose various regions differ only in temperature and surface blueness. In fact, it is a fascinating and varied place, with as many different habitat types as there are on land, and a huge variety of plants and animals.

The sea is also essential for the survival of all life, including human life, on Earth. Its plants help to regulate the atmosphere and provide oxygen for all animals to breathe. Its tides and currents shape the patterns of climate and weather that promote different types of plant and animal life on land.

We are still ignorant about many aspects of the sea, and this ignorance has led us to abuse the oceans, using them as dustbins and sewers, and overfishing marine life. Now we are beginning to discover the damage that has been, and continues to be, done to marine environments.

This book looks at the animals and plants that live in the oceans, and tells you about different sorts of marine habitats, how they work and the dangers they face from human activities. It also tells you how you can help give the oceans and their wildlife a future free from pollution and over-exploitation.

# Nations of the sea

## Earth's last wilderness

WHAT DOES THE SEA mean to you? Waves? Seabirds? A sandy shore? The sea is all these – and much more. It helps to shape our climate: whether it is warm or cold, wet or dry. And it is a vast, wild place filled with living things that are very different from those in our world of land and air.

Life in the sea was rich and complex for hundreds of millions of years before life on land got started, and today it is home for many thousands of distinct species of plants and animals.

Even with today's underwater technology, we don't know very much about the sea, which remains one of Earth's last great and beautiful wildernesses.

Top: A breaching killer whale looks small when it is seen against an expanse of blue water. This photograph illustrates the sea's first and most important defence against pollution: its vast size.
Above right: This is one of more than 500 species of feather star. We are only just beginning to find out about the strange and beautiful creatures that live in the oceans.
Above left: Many parts of the sea are still remote and inaccessible. Like this coral atoll, they remain unspoilt by human interference, even today.
Left: Many sea creatures are very productive and can recover fast from disaster.

### WILDSIDE WATCH

**Good news about the sea:**

- **The volume of the sea is over 1000 million cubic kilometers (more than 800 million cubic miles) so there is a vast quantity of water to dilute pollution.**
- **Many marine habitats are naturally unpredictable so the species who live in them have an inbuilt capacity to recover from man-made disasters like oil pollution or overfishing.**
- **Some parts of the sea are remote and inaccessible and remain unspoilt by human interference.**

# Rubbishing our seas

FOR AS LONG as man has existed, the sea has been used as a source of food, building materials, clothing, jewellery, medicine, and as a place to dump every sort of rubbish.

When the human population was small this did no harm. But now that there are five billion people on the planet, of whom 70 per cent live within 320 km (200 miles) of the coast, problems are becoming acute. Pollution from sewage and industrial wastes is poisoning our seas as we demand more cars and consumer goods. To satisfy our increasing appetite for the sea's products, overfishing is becoming common; even the sea bed is being mined for minerals.

Top: The sea is everybody's dustbin. Sewage and industrial waste are killing marine life all over the world.
Above: Improved technology allows us to catch more fish than ever before, but many marine creatures are now threatened as a result.
Above right: In many countries, population concentrates on the coasts to make use of the huge resources of the sea. As these populations expand, problems are created for marine life.
Right: Tankers roam the world to supply fuel for our cars. When they spill oil, seabirds like this guillemot pay the price.

**WILDSIDE WATCH**

**Bad news about the sea:**
- **The human population is rising, especially in poor countries which can't afford expensive methods of preventing pollution like sewage treatment works.**
- **Pollutants concentrate in coastal waters and enclosed seas and so are not diluted by mixing in huge oceans.**
- **Very little is known about marine life, and scientists are just beginning to discover the damage done to it by chemicals dumped in the sea.**

# Planet Ocean

MORE THAN 70 PER CENT of the Earth is covered by water, so perhaps a more appropriate name for our planet would be 'the Sea'. The land supports life on only part of its surface, and that life usually extends a mere couple of metres above and below the top of the soil.

The sea, on the other hand, is inhabited from its surface to its depths, which may reach 11,000 m (36,000 ft). It thus provides 99 per cent of all the planet's living space.

Although there are fewer natural (and artificial) barriers to movement in the sea than on the land, distance, depth, ocean currents and the shape of coastlines divide up the waters into a huge number of different habitats, each with its own distinctive plants and animals.

## A worldwide home

DEPTH, LOCATION, the availability of nutrients and distance from the coast are enough to create different habitats, but they are not absolute barriers: animals can wander. The young of many sea animals drift in ocean currents away from their birthplace until they find a similar home, which may be thousands of kilometres distant.

In this way, some marine organisms have spread all over the planet. Where on land a different species would play a similar role in each continent, in the sea one species might fill a niche worldwide.

It is therefore not surprising that of the five million or more species of plant and animal on Earth, only 250,000 are found in the sea.

**Right: Viewed from space, the Earth looks blue because it is almost covered by the sea. A visitor from space might call it 'planet Ocean'.**

# Patterns of growth

THE CONTENTS of a sample of sea life scooped up by a passing UFO would depend on where it was taken: how far from a pole or the equator, how far from the coast and at what depth.

A sample taken from the sunlit surface of the sea would be very different from one taken below 150 m (490 ft), where light can't reach, plants can't grow and life depends on the rain of dead bodies from above. Another sample, taken from the Arctic, where life almost stops in winter and bursts into activity in summer, would be different from one taken in the tropical sea where it is warm all year. And yet again, a sample taken from the coast where plants cling to the rocks would be different from one taken in the open ocean where tiny plankton float in the water.

The combinations of different depths, distance from coasts, and geographical location are almost infinite – and each combination describes a habitat in the sea.

Above: Seaweed, anchored to the shore and so held in the light, can grow big and create an underwater jungle that provides a home for many animals.
Right: Plant and animal plankton float in surface waters and are enormously productive: they are the source of food for all marine life.

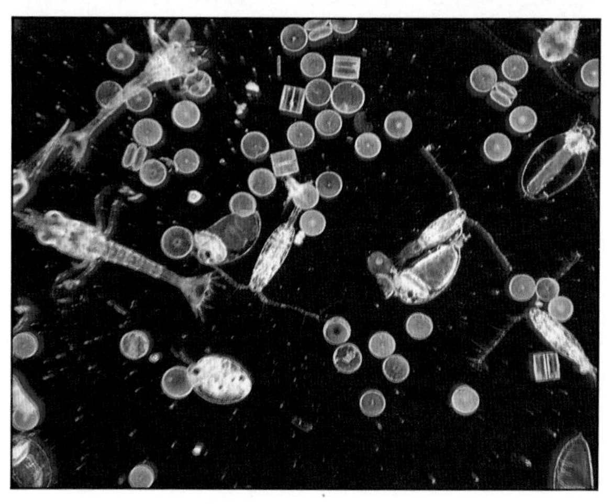

# The living sea

FROM BIG SEAWEEDS to tiny phytoplankton, sea plants, just like land plants, need nutrients as well as sunlight to be able to grow. Nutrients are plentiful in some parts of the sea and scarce in others, creating very different sorts of marine habitats.

Where ocean currents come up from the sea bed life-giving elements are brought to the surface waters to nourish plant growth and all the animals that feed on it. Large numbers of birds and animals congregate on these upwelling areas to feed and breed.

Much of the open ocean is a blue desert due to lack of nutrients. Yet coral reefs thrive in parts of this desert, growing well in warm, clear water and surviving by efficient recycling of scarce nutrients.

Seabirds like this gannet dive for fish in the productive waters near coasts and upwelling zones.

**WILDSIDE WATCH**

**What can you do to help save our seas?**

- **Remember that the biggest block to marine conservation is ignorance about the sea.**
- **Find out about the sea and the life it supports, and tell other people.**
- **Join an organisation that campaigns for marine conservation.**

# Poisons in the sea

POLLUTION IS THE GREATEST threat to marine life. All over the world, the sea is used as a free waste-disposal unit. Many chemicals we dump into the oceans do not break down, but accumulate in the bodies of sea creatures. The pollutants are passed on to other animals in the food chain, becoming more concentrated at every link. We are only beginning to discover the damage these and other wastes are doing to the sea.

## Too close to home

THE MOST POLLUTED parts of the sea are closest to the shore. Cities, farms, factories, and rivers that carry waste from far inland, all spill their rubbish into coastal waters.

Most countries dump untreated sewage straight into the sea. As sewage decays it deprives marine animals of vital oxygen. Its rich supply of nutrients also encourages the overgrowth of seaweeds, which remove yet more oxygen from the water.

In industrialised countries waste contains pesticides like DDT, chemicals called PCBs (from paints and glues) and 'heavy metals' (lead, cadmium, mercury) from factory and farm waste. At high concentrations these substances can kill marine life immediately, and at lower concentrations they gradually build up to cause long-term damage.

Nuclear power plants are often sited on the coast, and radioactive waste is released either deliberately into the sea or leaks accidentally. The Irish Sea, for example, is the most radioactive stretch of water in the world.

## The open sea

IT ISN'T ONLY coastal waters that are polluted. DDT can be found in the bodies of Antarctic penguins, because pesticides sprayed on crops and PCBs burnt on land are carried in the air all over the planet before dissolving in the sea. Deliberate dumping of harmful substances also takes place in the open sea in the form of sewage sludge and industrial pollutants. Perhaps more worrying still, are the radioactive wastes that, encased in concrete, have been dropped into deep ocean trenches.

These wastes are potentially dangerous even after hundreds of thousands of years have passed.

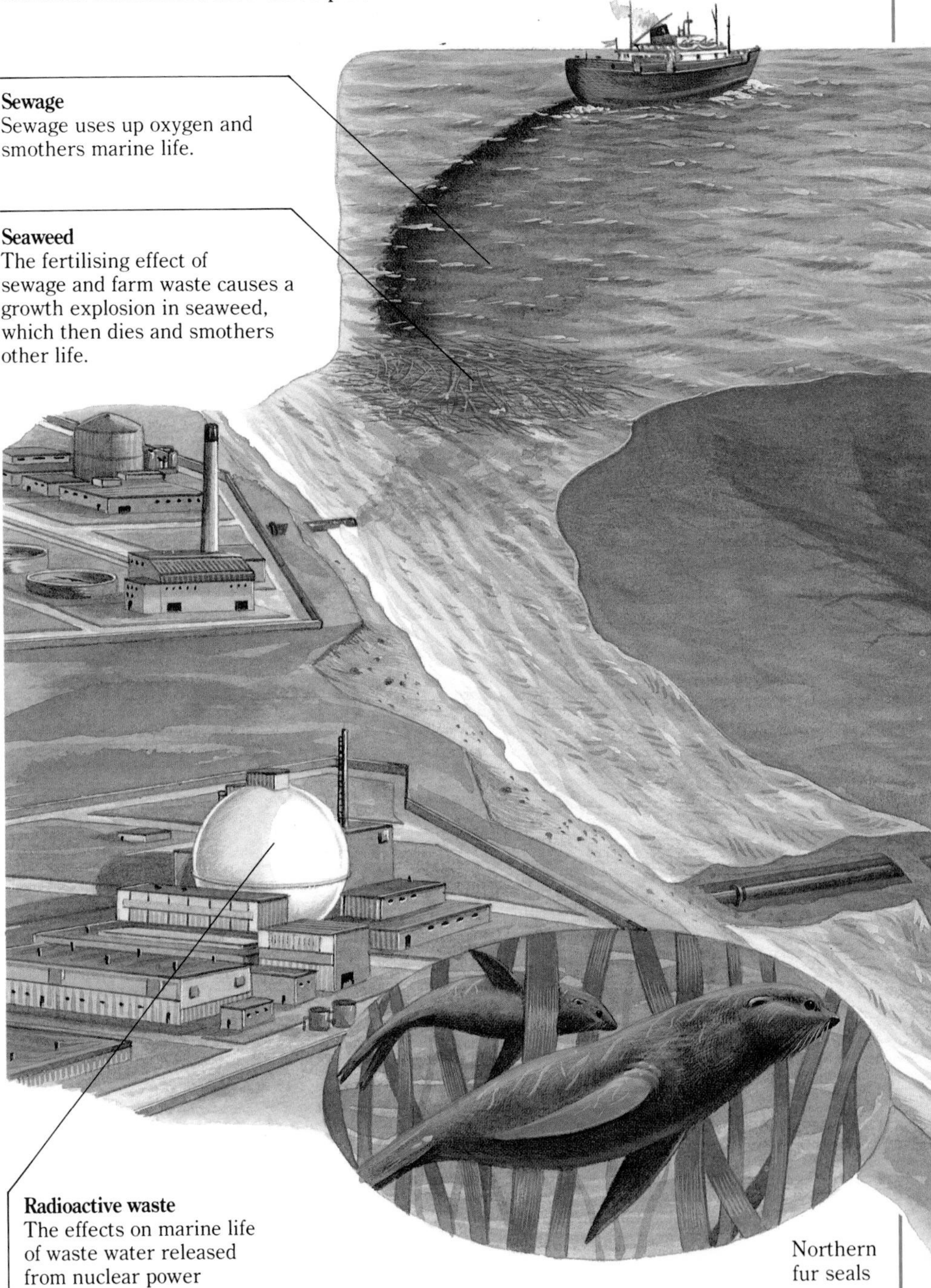

**Sewage**
Sewage uses up oxygen and smothers marine life.

**Seaweed**
The fertilising effect of sewage and farm waste causes a growth explosion in seaweed, which then dies and smothers other life.

**Radioactive waste**
The effects on marine life of waste water released from nuclear power stations, or spent fuel wrapped in concrete that leaks radioactivity, are poorly understood. It is known that they are long-lasting.

Northern fur seals

**PCBs**
Seals and other sea mammals fail to breed and their resistance to disease is reduced as a result of pollution by these chemicals. Because the animals are near the end of marine food chains, they accumulate the chemicals in their bodies. Many species worldwide are affected.

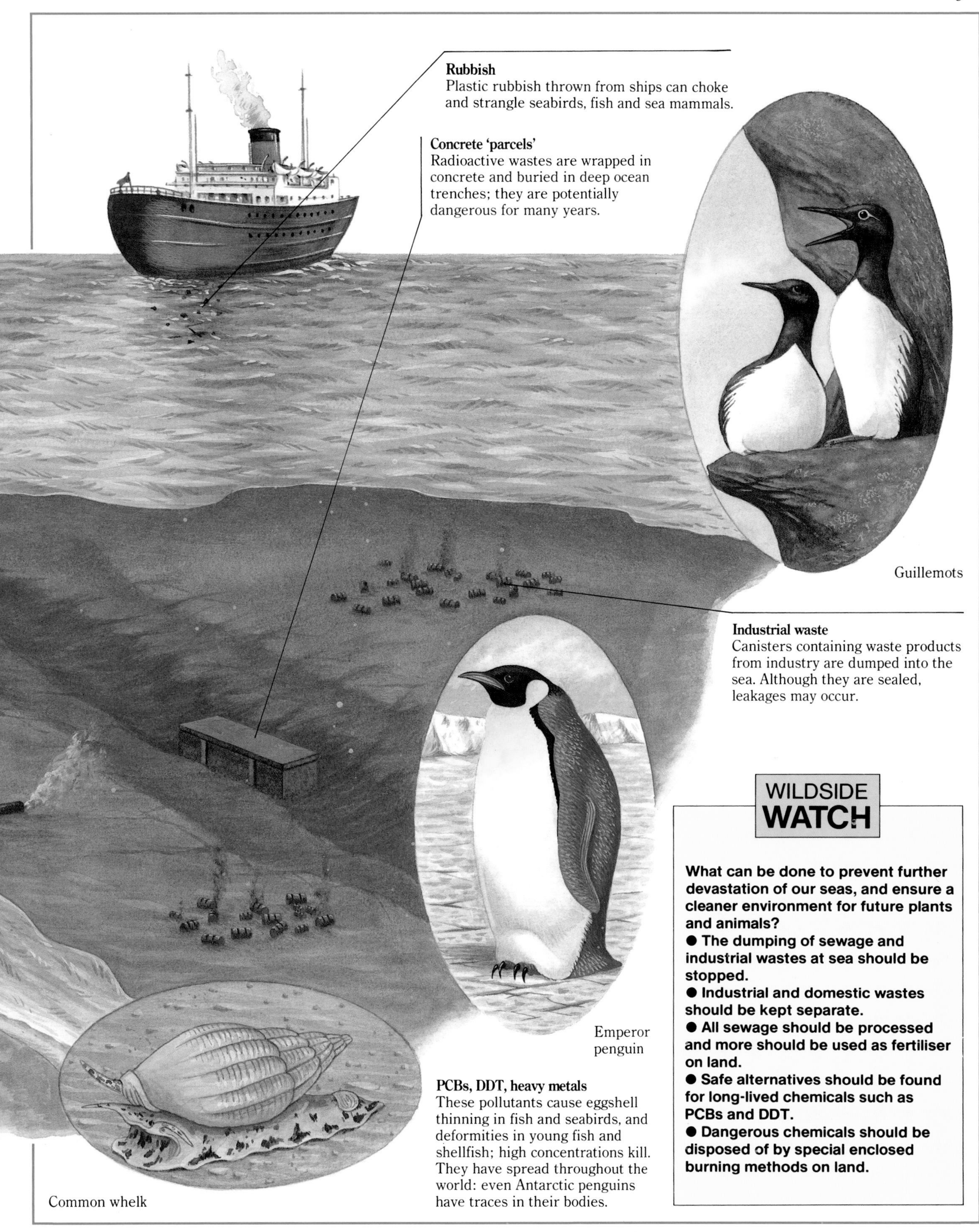

**Rubbish**
Plastic rubbish thrown from ships can choke and strangle seabirds, fish and sea mammals.

**Concrete 'parcels'**
Radioactive wastes are wrapped in concrete and buried in deep ocean trenches; they are potentially dangerous for many years.

Guillemots

**Industrial waste**
Canisters containing waste products from industry are dumped into the sea. Although they are sealed, leakages may occur.

Emperor penguin

**PCBs, DDT, heavy metals**
These pollutants cause eggshell thinning in fish and seabirds, and deformities in young fish and shellfish; high concentrations kill. They have spread throughout the world: even Antarctic penguins have traces in their bodies.

Common whelk

**WILDSIDE WATCH**

**What can be done to prevent further devastation of our seas, and ensure a cleaner environment for future plants and animals?**

- **The dumping of sewage and industrial wastes at sea should be stopped.**
- **Industrial and domestic wastes should be kept separate.**
- **All sewage should be processed and more should be used as fertiliser on land.**
- **Safe alternatives should be found for long-lived chemicals such as PCBs and DDT.**
- **Dangerous chemicals should be disposed of by special enclosed burning methods on land.**

# Blue water...

PRINCE WILLIAM SOUND is a huge bay on the west coast of Alaska surrounded by ice-capped mountains and glaciers. It is one of the most beautiful places on Earth. There are few human settlements and almost everyone is a fisherman.

Since 1977 Prince William Sound has been the terminus of the trans-Alaska oil pipeline which carries crude oil from wells on the north coast 800 miles overland, to be shipped out by tankers. Each tanker carries tens of millions of gallons, and 900 tanker loads pass through the Sound's treacherous waters every year.

## Not just a pretty face

PRINCE WILLIAM SOUND isn't just beautiful, it is teeming with life. Its 6500 sq. km (2500 square miles) of open sea water are full of nutrients and oxygen and in summer these promote a huge bloom of the microscopic plants that are called plankton.

In one way or another, the plankton supports 200 different species of birds, at least four different species of salmon and 11 different species of marine mammal, including sea otters, killer whales, stellar sea lions and the Dall's porpoise. In spring, the Sound's resident animals are joined by migrants from the south: humpbacked whales, grey whales and 15 million shore birds. By the end of March these visitors have begun to arrive and residents, like birds and sea otters, are ready to have their young in time for the abundance of summer food. Such was the scene at the end of March 1989.

**Right: Prince William Sound in Alaska, before the Exxon oil spill in March 1989. It was full of life - both animal and human.**

**Tufted puffin**
These puffins winter offshore and come to land to breed in the spring.

**Dall's porpoise**
A fast swimmer, the Dall's porpoise dives deep to hunt for squid and fish.

**Stellar sea lion**
Lives all year in Prince William Sound, mostly within 45 km (28 miles) of the shore.

**WILDSIDE WATCH**

**Modern societies depend on oil to fuel cars and industry.**
- **Oil is taken round the world in huge tanker ships.**
- **Many tankers are old and in bad condition.**
- **Coral reefs, mangroves and polar marine habitats are badly damaged when polluted with oil.**
- **A big tanker needs at least 3 km (2 miles) of open water to stop.**
- **Almost no coastline is far from these tanker routes.**

**What you can do:**
- **Walk or cycle or use public transport instead of a car. The less oil we use, the less we need to transport on the sea.**

This sea otter is having its fur cleaned at a rehabilitation centre, but many others were not so lucky. They died of cold because their oil-matted fur no longer insulated them.

Some bald eagles died when they ate the bodies of other oiled animals, swallowed the oil and were poisoned. Others were themselves covered in oil.

# . . . Black death

JUST BEFORE ONE O'CLOCK in the morning of 24 March 1989 the oil tanker *Exxon Valdez* ran aground on rocks at the north end of Prince William Sound, and 11 million gallons of crude oil poured out through massive holes in her hull. Wind and currents spread the oil over huge areas of sea and at least 2000 km (1200 miles) of shore. By the end of the summer the oil had killed 100,000 birds, including 150 bald eagles, more than 1000 sea otters and whole communities of seaweeds and shore life. It is impossible to estimate how many seals, sea lions or whales died as their dead bodies sink to the sea bottom.

## Why are oil slicks deadly?

CRUDE OIL is the stuff that pipelines and most oil tankers carry. It is a mixture of substances, including petrol, engine oil and tar. When crude oil spills into the sea it spreads over the surface and some of the most poisonous parts, such as petrol, evaporate. Animals inhale these poisonous fumes, which cause damage to lungs, livers and nerves. The heavier oil and tar coat fur and feathers, leading to cold and shock and eventually death. If swallowed they, too, are poisonous.

In less than three days, waves and wind whip up the rest of the oil into a thick foam known as 'chocolate mousse'. This smothers shores and wildlife for months before it breaks down, leaving tar balls to wash up on beaches. Before the 'mousse' stage, oil can be scooped up, contained or dissolved using toxic chemicals called dispersants. Fast action before the 'mousse' stage prevents much destruction, but action after the *Exxon Valdez* spill was slow.

Above: A huge rescue operation was mounted to clean up beaches after the Exxon spill. But it came too late to save many birds and animals.

Auks like puffins and murres dive to escape the oil, only to surface in yet another patch and die as a result.

# Long-term effects

MANY BIRDS, mammals and fish are killed immediately by an oil spill, but oil can go on killing for months and years because it disrupts the ability of animals to fight disease. It can also affect breeding so that no healthy young are reared successfully.

By the end of the summer of 1989 some of the lasting scars of the disaster could be seen in Prince William Sound. Many bald eagles failed to breed because their eggs and young had been poisoned with oil, and marine mammals showed signs of damaged internal organs. But there were hopeful signs too: the plankton bloom was good and many fish spawned as normal.

Only long-term studies of the Sound will keep track of the lasting effects of the spill. Perhaps the best hope for the future lies in the sea's unpredictability which gives marine creatures a natural ability to adapt to changing conditions. Prince William Sound may heal, but no one knows how long it will take.

Top: The *Amoco Cadiz* foundered on the coast of Brittany in France in 1978, spilling 220,000 tonnes of crude oil. Thousands of seabirds died and kilometres of coast were smothered in 'chocolate mousse'. Above: Ten years on, life was almost back to normal. But how many more times can the sea recover?

**WILDSIDE WATCH**

**Every year six million tonnes of oil is spilt into the world's oceans. Most comes from the 'normal operation' of tankers and pipelines. And most spills are small – but even they kill wildlife.**

**What can be done?**

- **Improve the standard of training for tanker and pipeline crews.**
- **Get rid of old tanker ships and equipment.**
- **Stop deliberate oil pollution from the washing of tanks.**

**What you can do:**

- **Write to one or more of the oil companies and ask what they are doing to prevent marine pollution.**

# On the rocks

ROCKY SHORES OFFER marine plants and animals a secure anchorage in the sunlit and nutrient-rich waters closest to the surface of coastal seas. But life in this prime spot has its disadvantages as well as advantages because the shore species are exposed to air, sun, wind, rain and frost.

On tropical and polar coasts the extremes of heat and cold keep most life below the low-tide mark and shores look rather bare. But rocky shores in temperate places are covered with life, forming some of the world's most fascinating communities of marine species.

## Maintaining the balance

SHORE INHABITANTS eat each other and get eaten, they compete for space and are washed away by storms. All this constant change creates a living balance that maintains the huge variety of life on a healthy rocky shore. It also means that the plants and animals of the shore are linked together in complicated ways so that upsetting one species can have an effect on many others. Even quite mild pollution can alter this balance by killing just one plant or animal.

**Breaking the chain**

Starfish and dog whelks eat mussels.

Barnacles, limpets, seaweeds and many other species colonise the space left when the mussels have been eaten.

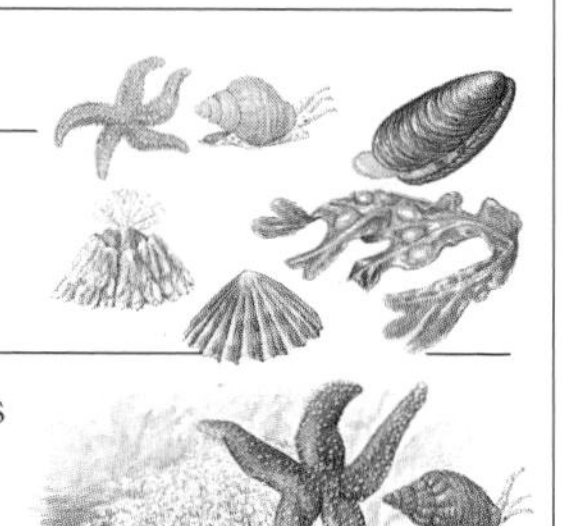

Power-station hot water kills the dog whelks and starfish. Without these predators to keep their numbers low, mussels take over and species variety is lost.

### WILDSIDE WATCH

**Here are a few ways to discover the world 'on the rocks' when you next visit the seaside.**

- **Look at the shore from a distance. Can you see a distinct pattern of seaweeds or bare patches of rock that reveal separate zones?**
- **Walk down to the sea, stop every 10 paces and see how many kinds of life you can spot. You'll find different groups of plants and animals in different parts of the shore.**
- **Look out for signs of pollution by oil, sewage, chemicals. Write down or photograph what you see and report it to your local councillor or government representative, and to your local newspaper.**

## Competing for space

TRY CLAMBERING OVER a rocky shore at low tide, from the land to the edge of the sea. At first you'll be moving over almost bare rocks, then quite dense seaweed. You'll see that the shore is divided up into quite definite bands, or zones, with particular seaweeds and animals characteristic of each one.

The exact composition and size of each zone depends on what coast you are on, but you can see zonation in action all over the world. This is because zonation is caused by two things that happen on every rocky shore: competition and exposure. Competition for space on the best parts of the shore, those covered by the sea for longest, is very intense, and only the very well-adapted animals and plants keep their places.

This drives some species further up the shore, where they must stand greater exposure to the air. So at the top of the shore are the animals that can survive exposure but not competition, and at the bottom are the skilful competitors.

**Sewage dumped in the sea over-fertilises green seaweed, which grows and smothers shore life.**

**Middle shore**

The middle shore is exposed twice a day for a few hours. The tide moves fast, so plants and animals are battered by the waves. Life is more varied and abundant than on higher zones, and competition between species is fiercer. This region is dominated by brown wrack seaweeds that dislike exposure and provide shelter for animals. The common periwinkle spawns into the sea; it shelters under weed or seals its open shell with mucus to prevent drying. Dog whelks eat limpets. Soft-bodied animals like sea anemones live in crevices and pools.

**Lower shore**

The lower shore is exposed only at the lowest tides, perhaps only a few times in a month or even a year. It is the richest of the zones with many species. Seaweeds and soft-bodied animals that cannot survive exposure inhabit this region, competing with each other and with more thoroughly marine species. Large kelp seaweeds create a forest for other plants and animals. Filter-feeders like mussels, which are found in higher zones, grow bigger and faster here. Starfish replace dog whelks as the predators of shellfish.

**Splash zone**
Permanently exposed and lashed with salt spray, the splash zone is home to few species, which are almost independent of the sea. The small periwinkle is a marine snail that has evolved a simple lung, but releases its eggs into the sea. Bristletails are primitive land insects and the sea slater is a crustacean that looks like a wood louse.

Sea slater

Bristletail

Encrusting lichens

Small periwinkle

**Upper shore**
The highest regions of the upper shore are exposed for 24 hours or even several days at a time, and covered by the sea for only a few hours. Channelled wrack seaweed has oil in its fronds to help it stop drying out completely. Barnacles shut tight when exposed and open to filter food particles from the water when the tide covers them. The rough periwinkle incubates eggs inside the female's body, protecting them from drying.

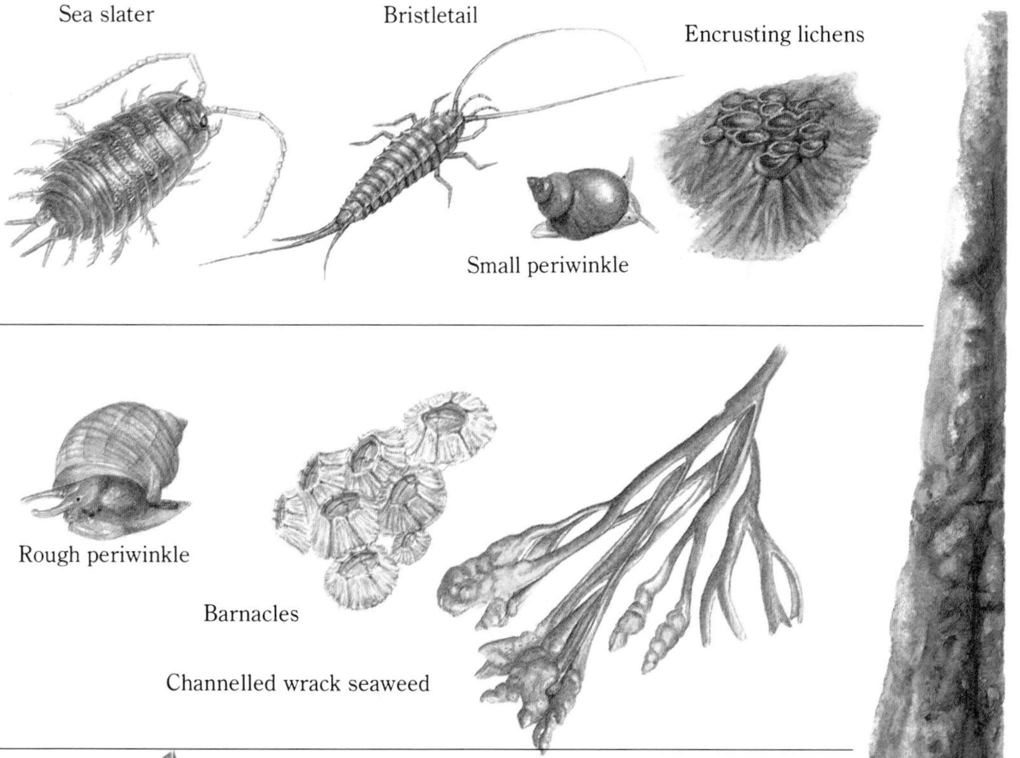

Rough periwinkle

Barnacles

Channelled wrack seaweed

Sea mats and hydroids on seaweeds

Chiton

Limpet

Wrack seaweed

Dog whelk

Common periwinkle

Sea anemone

Starfish

Sea slug

Brittle stars

Sponges

# The silver strand

AT FIRST GLANCE a beach may look lifeless because no plant or animal can cling easily to the unstable surface of the sand. However, many animals live beneath it, protected from rough waves and drying air.

Worms, crabs and molluscs are all residents, burrowing even further down to filter food from the sand and the sea. In their turn, they serve as prey for visitors to the beach who come to eat or to breed.

But animals that live protected in the sand are threatened everywhere by human activities.

## More waste

RAW HUMAN SEWAGE is emptied into coastal seas all over the world, but European beaches, because they are visited by such huge numbers of tourists, are amongst the worst affected. The sewage decays in the shallow water, using up the dissolved oxygen and suffocating the animals in the sand beneath.

With the tourists come anglers who use sand-living worms for bait. Millions of worms are collected by professional 'diggers', which drastically reduces populations, disrupts the habitat of other sand creatures and releases buried pollution.

**Tourists crowd coastal resorts and increase the amount of raw sewage dumped on the beaches.**

**Common cockle**
The common cockle lies just under the sand and filters food particles from the water with a siphon.

**Burrowing starfish**
The burrowing starfish preys on worms and molluscs that live under the sand.

**Lug worm**
The pencil-size lug worm lives in a U-shape burrow. It swallows sand from which it extracts food.

# Unlucky horseshoe crabs

EVERY MAY the beaches of Delaware Bay on the east coast of North America are covered with horseshoe crabs. They are not true crabs, but unlikely relatives of spiders. The horseshoes come to the bay's shores to lay their eggs, which form a vital source of food for millions of wading birds migrating along the coast.

A hundred years ago the crabs were far more abundant than they are today. Their numbers were reduced when up to five million of them were collected each year to be made into livestock feed. This was stopped in the 1950s, some beaches were protected, and the crab population is now showing signs of recovery.

**Hundreds of millions of horseshoe crabs on America's east coast were killed in the late nineteenth and early twentieth centuries. Their populations may still be recovering.**

# Raiding the sand

PALM-FRINGED TROPICAL BEACHES are populated by many different sorts of crab. They run about on the sea's edge scavenging for food and burrowing into the sand for protection. The crabs and all other beach-living animals are simply swept aside when their home is dug up to provide sand for building a new hotel or airport runway. Of course poor countries with tropical beaches want to earn money from tourism, but ironically they are destroying their tourist attractions in order to do it.

**Tourism now threatens the wildlife of some tropical beaches. It has destroyed animal and plant life on many shores in Europe and America.**

**Sanderlings and horseshoe crabs**
During their two-week stop-over on Delaware Bay, 50,000 sanderlings eat 27 tonnes of horseshoe-crab eggs.

**Sand crabs**
These are two examples of sand-living crabs. The tiny sand-bubbler crab collects balls of sand and scrapes minute edible particles off the grains. The ghost crab lives in burrows in the sand and eats the remains of plankton left by the waves.

**WILDSIDE WATCH**

**Beaches are vanishing all over the world – and their wildlife with them. Make sure you conserve the animal and plant life on the beaches you visit.**

- **Don't disturb or damage wildlife when you visit a beach.**
- **Take your rubbish home with you, or put it in a litter-bin.**
- **Keep your holidays simple: stay away from high-rise resorts that drive away animals and harm plant life.**

# Beside the seaside

PEOPLE HAVE ALWAYS loved seaside holidays. This is bad news for all sorts of sea life but amongst the worst affected are sea turtles. They roam the world's warmer oceans and lay their eggs on sandy beaches, which they now have to share with tourists. The problem is particularly bad in the Mediterranean where turtles have been driven from one beach after another by the 100 million people who visit its shores every year.

## Turtle's tourist nightmare

A FEMALE LOGGERHEAD TURTLE crawls from the waves on to a sandy beach on a Greek island. She spends her life out at sea, but now she must come ashore to bury her eggs where warm sand will incubate them. She waited for night to fall just offshore with other females. They had to dodge the speedboats and the water skiers all day. As she struggles up the beach, lights flash from cars among the dunes, noise pours from the tavernas. Terrified, some females turn back to the sea where their eggs pour out into the sea water where they die.

At last, our female finds a patch of sand that has not been packed rock hard by the cars and feet of tourists. She digs her nest and lays her 150 golf-ball-sized eggs. By dawn she has finished burying the eggs and returns to the sea. In the 50 or 60 days before they hatch, her eggs may be crushed by human sunbathers. If they survive, the young may be trapped by hard-packed sand, or they may die as street lights at night distract them from the shine of the sea and draw them inland.

**Far right: A female loggerhead turtle returns to the sea after laying her eggs. Eggs and young have always been at risk from predators; now tourist activities also threaten their survival (right).**

# Fun for people...not wildlife

WORLDWIDE, six of the seven species of marine turtles are already endangered through hunting and egg collection. Extra pressure caused by tourists visiting nesting beaches could prove disastrous.

All sorts of animal species can be damaged by people enjoying their seaside holidays. Speedboats and windsurfers in Hawaii pass over female humpback whales and their newborn calves, driving them into less sheltered waters, where conditions are less than ideal for survival of the calves.

Windsurfers can sail into landlocked bays and shallow waters where boats can't go, disturbing wildlife. On the Ythan estuary in Scotland groups of eider ducklings, too young to fly, may become exhausted through avoiding windsurfers. Hotels, marinas, cars, litter and sheer numbers of feet and bodies mean that wildlife and large-scale tourism don't mix.

Marram, a special sand-loving grass, holds dunes together so that animals and plants can colonise them. People's feet erode the grass, and the dune and its ecosystem blow away - unless the sand is held and replanted with marram, as here in East Anglia, England.

**WILDSIDE WATCH**

**Here is how some countries are helping their turtles:**

- **Controlling hunting and egg collecting.**
- **Banning trade in turtle shells.**
- **Protecting eggs and young turtles on beaches from predators and people.**

**Be green on the beach and on holiday:**

- **Find out about the wildlife of the beach you visit.**
- **Don't disturb wildlife in or out of the water.**
- **Don't buy souvenirs made of animals.**
- **Live simply - luxury resorts are bad for wildlife.**

# Where rivers meet the sea

**Boats and leisure**
Marinas for sail boats and docks for commercial shipping are built on estuaries, which means there is less food and space for birds. Fuel oil and cargoes bring pollution. Anti-fouling paints on ships' hulls contain TBT (Tributyle tin) which washes out and poisons invertebrates and fish in the estuary.

WHEN A RIVER FLOWS into the sea it slows down and fresh water mixes with salt water. This mixing and slowing makes both types of water drop their loads of silt and bits of plant and animal matter to the bottom. Year by year more deposits build up, creating mudflats and saltmarshes. So an estuary is made, and it is a highly desirable habitat for animals and people.

## Mud, mud, glorious mud!

MUD IS THE SOURCE of an estuary's wealth. It is full of organic material, such as broken-up leaves and seaweed, animal faeces and bodies, providing perfect food for all sorts of animals. Worms swallow mud to extract it, molluscs filter water to catch it and crustaceans scrape it off the mud surface to eat it.

New supplies of food are brought in all the time by the river and the tides, supplying enough nutrients for more than half a kilogram (one pound) of invertebrate life for every square metre (square yard) of mud. The mud-eaters become food for huge numbers of birds when the tide is out and for fish when it is in, making estuaries some of the world's most important wildlife habitats.

**High-tide feeders**
Fish swim up the estuary to feed, and seals follow them. Both fish and seals may use its shelter to breed. Seven out of America's 10 most commercially important fish and shellfish depend on estuaries for food and breeding.

**Pollution**
Any waste discharged into a river ends up in its estuary. Sewage dumped there uses up oxygen in the water so that animals suffocate; industrial waste from oil refineries and factories, which are often built on estuaries, kills immediately or by long-term poisoning.

**Land reclamation**
Estuaries are drained to make dry land on which factories, farms, houses or even airports can be built. As a result there is less food for birds, which may starve in winter or be too thin to breed in the spring.

**Estuary mud-munchers**
There are only a few estuarine invertebrate species. But numbers can be huge: on one British estuary there were 36,000 grape-pip size snails, 22,000 tiny crustaceans and 220 fat pencil-size worms in every square metre (square yard) of mud.

**Food for winter, fuel for travel**
Millions of wading birds, ducks and geese spend their winters on estuaries, or use them as feeding stop-overs on their migrations. A single estuary can be essential to whole populations: the Wadden See off the Dutch coast feeds half of Europe's teal, curlew and other species in winter.

**WILDSIDE WATCH**

**Human activities put estuaries at risk in many parts of the world. This threatens the birds and other animals that use them as breeding areas or stopping-places during migration.**

- **Some estuaries are reclaimed for agriculture, forestry or fish farming.**
- **Rivers that form the estuaries may be channelled into canals or re-routed.**

**What you can do:**

- **Monitor the birds and animals in your local estuary.**
- **Look for signs of pollution and disturbance.**
- **Join an organisation that campaigns to save estuaries.**

# The seal scare

SEWAGE, PESTICIDES, heavy metals, even radioactive waste: all get dumped into the sea. Most is deliberately dumped; the rest reaches the sea via polluted rivers. It is assumed that all these unpleasant substances will be washed away and diluted by the vast volume of the sea, but the coastal waters where most dumping takes place are relatively shallow and some, like those of the North Sea, are fairly enclosed. The result is that pollutants are not washed away or diluted; instead they slowly poison the sea and its inhabitants.

## Poisoned links

PCBS, POLYCHLORINATED BIPHENOLS, are the by-product of industrial processes like making paints.

Dumped into rivers and seas, the chemicals are absorbed by plankton and become ever more concentrated with every link in the food chain.

At the top of the chain, seals get a large dose of PCBs, reducing their resistance to disease and their ability to breed. So it is no surprise that the numbers of seals in the Wadden See, off the coasts of the Netherlands, Germany and Denmark, dropped from 1500 in 1964 to 500 in 1974 because PCBs had stopped many females from having pups.

Also, between 1988 and 1989 over 17,000 common, or harbour, seals died from a new viral disease in the North Sea, perhaps because PCBs had lowered their resistance.

Below: In the North Sea, seals' resistance to disease has been lowered by pollution. Many succumbed to a deadly virus in 1988 and 1989. Bottom: Common seals bask on the North Sea coast. They carry a load of poisons in their bodies, the result of pollution by humans.

# Europe's dustbin

THE NORTH SEA receives wastes from at least six countries, wastes that damage the marine environment in all sorts of ways. As sewage decays, for example, it uses up oxygen in the water, with the result that fish and invertebrates suffocate. Sewage also encourages the growth of huge blooms of toxic microscopic plants that can poison vast areas. Heavy metals, like mercury and cadmium from industrial pollution, are other potential killers that have been found at high levels in the bodies of fish, birds and seals.

Of all the pollutants, pesticides may be the most common. They poison plankton, fish eggs and larvae, and make the eggshells of sea birds too thin. What is this poisonous cocktail doing to the creatures of the North Sea? Numbers of dolphins and harbour porpoises have dropped, some stocks of fish are declining and, most sinister of all, many flatfish sampled in the North Sea had cancerous growths and skin diseases.

Is pollution the cause? We are only just beginning to find out.

**FILLING THE DUSTBIN**

Over 65.5 million tonnes of pollutants are dumped or spilt into the North Sea every year.

**Oil spills**
From ships 60,000 tonnes
From rigs 30,000 tonnes

**Chemicals**
From ships 2800 tonnes
From rivers Nitrates 1,166,567 tonnes
Phosphates 266,719 tonnes
Cadmium, lead, zinc, copper, mercury 13,179 tonnes

**Industrial waste burned at sea**
95,800 tonnes

**Radioactive waste**
5500 TBq/yr

**The following are dumped at sea:**
Dredged materials 55,257,000 tonnes
Liquid industrial waste 1,679,356 tonnes
Coal and ash from power stations 1,944,421 tonnes
Sewage 5,077,000 tonnes

**Atmospheric pollution**
626,600 tonnes (estimated) from factories, power stations and farming

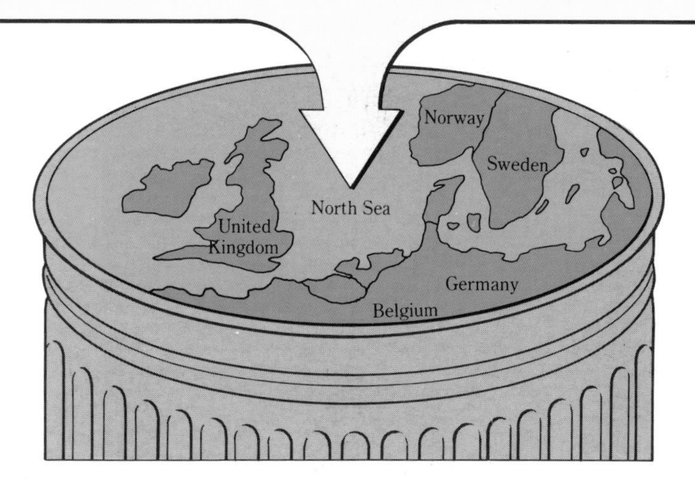


**WILDSIDE WATCH**

**Pollution of the seas by plastic products is also a worldwide problem:**

- **All sorts of plastic containers and packaging, 45 million kg (100 million lb) of it, is dumped in the sea every year by beach-goers and people on boats.**
- **Every year one million seabirds and 100,000 marine mammals are killed when they swallow plastic or get caught in it.**

**What you can do:**

- **Take all your rubbish home from the beach or the boat.**

# Seabirds ashore

THERE ARE OVER 280 different species of seabirds, from the tiny Least storm petrel that weighs just 25 g (less than 1 oz) to the emperor penguin, which stands 1.2 m (4 ft) tall and weighs over 30 kg (70 lb). All are adapted to a life roaming the oceans. They have wings for non-stop flying or for propelling themselves underwater, and feet that serve as paddles.

But seabirds must return to the land to breed, where their paddle feet and awkward wings make them clumsy and vulnerable to land predators. To spread the risk of becoming prey they often nest in colonies. They are not out of danger, however, because they may form a rich source of food for people and also be wiped out by man-made changes to their habitat.

## Nesting on top of a volcano

ALBATROSSES ARE PERHAPS the most oceanic of all seabirds, gliding over the waves for years at a time. There are 14 different species, the most endangered of which is the short-tailed albatross, once seen nesting in hundreds of thousands on islands in the north Pacific. Adults were killed for meat and feathers and by the 1930s just 100 birds remained. They are now protected, but nest only on the tiny Japanese island of Torishima, where numbers have risen to around 200. Even here they are not out of danger: Torishima is an active volcano and an eruption in the breeding season could wipe out the whole species.

**Below: Albatrosses, often seen hundreds of miles from land and in fearsome storms, have given rise to countless superstitions. One of the best known, that it is unlucky to kill an albatross, is the basis of Samuel Taylor Coleridge's poem, 'The Rime of the Ancient Mariner'.**

Short-tailed albatross

## Home, dangerous home

SEABIRDS REDUCE the dangers of nesting on land by choosing remote islands or sea clffs, where there are no natural predators. But this is a poor defence against people and the animals that we bring with us, such as rats and cats. Also, although most seabirds hatch only one or two chicks, even these small broods need lots of food to grow. Nesting seabirds may therefore rely on a source of food close to shore – just where humans may be taking it all by overfishing.

**Cahow: vanished habitat**
Bermuda is a holiday paradise and tourist developments cover what were once cahow, or Bermuda petrel, breeding habitats.

**Abbots booby: threatened by mining**
Abbots booby nests are found only on Christmas Island in the north-east Indian Ocean, high in the trees. Some of these sites are inside a reserve, but phosphate mining threatens many of them.

**Marbled murrelet: where will it nest?**
Marbled murrelets nest alone, sometimes kilometres inland in the great ancient 'old growth forests' of Alaska. These forests, and the nesting sites, are now threatened by clear felling. Thousands of murrelets die each year, trapped in gillnets set for salmon, and in small-scale oil spills on shipping routes.

# Saving seabirds

THE MOST EFFECTIVE way to protect seabirds is to stop the exploitation and disturbance of their nest sites by human beings. The removal of introduced animals is also important: rats and cats take the eggs and the young, and goats and cattle trample and destroy nests. Other measures depend on the species. The number of cahows, for example, has increased since special 'collars' on their nest-burrow entrances were fitted to keep marauding tropical birds out.

And, of course, we can all do our bit by avoiding breeding grounds when we visit the seaside.

**Information is the conservationist's most important tool. To learn about migration and longevity, biologists identify birds with leg rings.**

**WILDSIDE WATCH**

**What is needed for the conservation of seabirds around the world?**

- **More information on which species breed where, in what numbers and how successfully.**
- **Legal protection and reserves set up specifically for seabirds.**
- **The removal of introduced predators, such as cats, rats, and goats, from all nest sites.**
- **Control of oil spills and other pollution near breeding areas.**
- **Greater awareness on the part of fishermen to prevent the exploitation of seabirds and their accidental deaths in fishing gear.**

# Otters, urchins and abalones

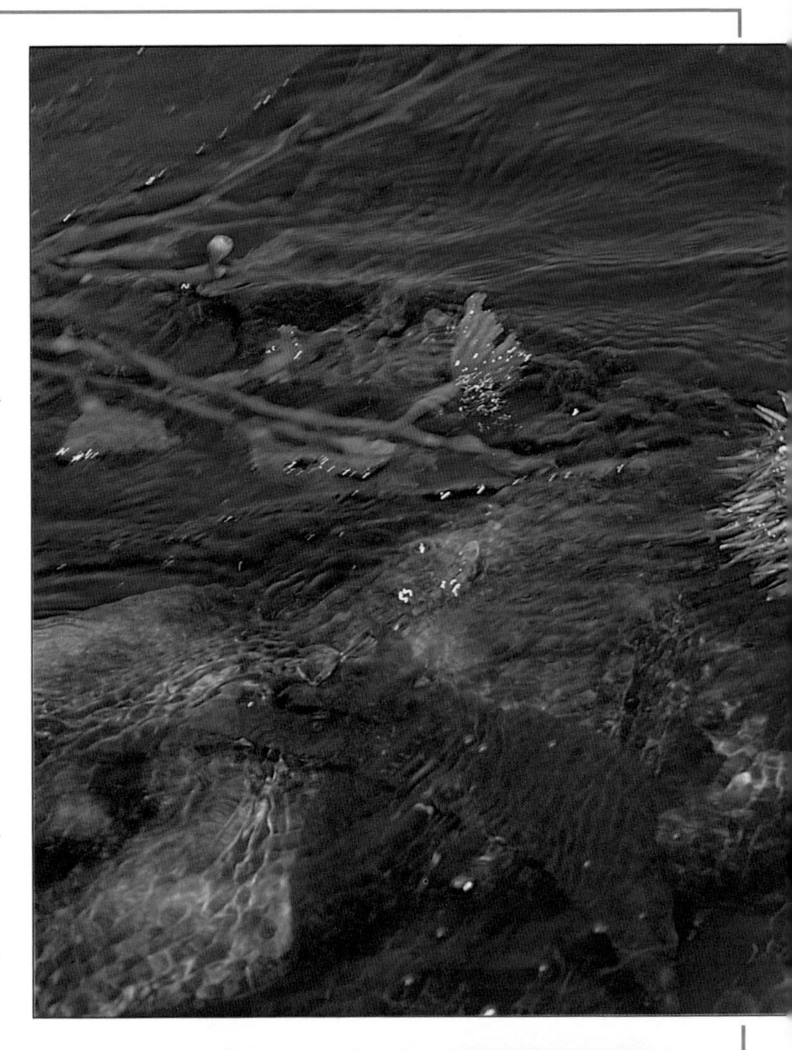

LOOK OUT TO SEA at low tide from a rocky shore in any of the cooler parts of the world. Beyond the line of the surf you may see tips of huge seaweed fronds breaking the surface of the water. You are looking at the topmost branches of a forest of the giant seaweeds called kelps.

Constantly covered in cool sunlit water and supplied with fresh nutrients by the waves, kelps are in a plant heaven where they grow big and create a habitat for all sorts of animals, from sea slugs to sea otters.

## Fishermen's friends?

A SEA OTTER floating on its back in a kelp bed may look beautiful to us, but to a Californian fisherman it is a threat. Sea otters have expensive tastes: they love abalone and other shellfish worth millions of dollars to the fishing industry.

Californian sea otters are rare, there are only about 1500 of them. What concerns fishermen are the recent attempts by conservationists to expand their range by moving animals into new areas, reducing the risk of the whole population being wiped out by an oil spill. Fishermen are demanding otter-free areas, which could mean that colonies may be culled to stop them expanding into these zones.

But if otters were allowed to spread unchecked fishermen could benefit, because kelp needs sea otters, and a healthy kelp forest is home to commercially valuable fish and shellfish. When Pacific sea otters were almost wiped out by nineteenth-century fur hunters, kelp declined too. Evidence suggests that this is because another favourite meal of sea otters is sea urchins, which eat kelp.

Without otters to eat the urchins, whole forests can disappear. Californian sea otters have been protected since the 1930s and kelp has recovered with them. Old forests have grown bigger and more vigorous and new forests have sprung up.

**Above right: Sea otters dive to depths of up to 40 m (130 ft) in search of abalone and other food. Back on the surface, they use their chests as tables and use stones to crack shells open.**

**Right: Californian sea otters are captured and taken to areas where they lived 200 years ago, to establish new colonies. Radio tags help conservationists to retrieve wanderers from fishermen's otter-free zones.**

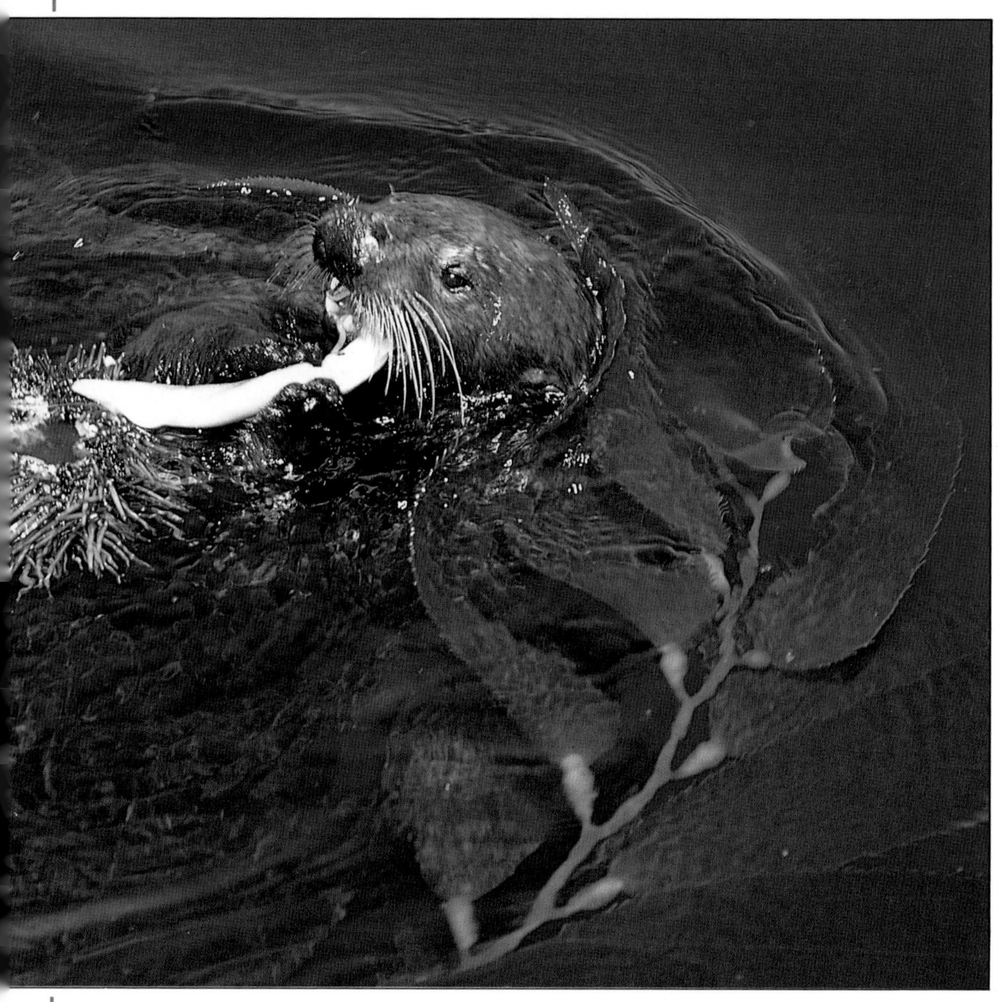

Giant kelp:
50 m (165 ft)

A common British and European kelp (Laminaria digitata): 1–3 m (3–10 ft)

# Same play, different actors

THE STORY OF THE giant kelp and the Californian sea otter is repeated all over the world. The kelps and animals are different, but the parts that they play are similar. In Alaska, at the northern end of the sea otters' range, kelp forests grow only where the otters can dive. Everywhere else, sea urchins graze the kelp to nothing.

In Nova Scotia, overfishing of lobsters, a major predator on sea urchins, caused an urchin epidemic that cleared kelp forests along 15km (9 miles) of coastline. South African sea urchins are kept in check by lobsters, octopus, dogfish, seals – and waves that move kelp fronds out of the urchins' reach.

**All kinds of kelp**
Kelp comes in many different shapes and sizes. The giant kelp from California is the biggest: 50 m (165 ft) long – or more.

Palm kelp:
10–30 cm (4–12 in)

**WILDSIDE WATCH**

**Sea otters are found in the north Pacific Ocean, but even though they are far away, you can help to conserve these fascinating creatures.**

- **Write to one or more of the oil companies and ask what they are doing to prevent pollution. Sea otters rely on their fur to keep warm, and freeze to death if it is covered in oil.**
- **Join an international organisation that includes conserving sea otters in its aims.**
- **If you live in America, join a national organisation that promotes sea-otter conservation.**

# Paddling trees

MANY OF THE WORLD'S tropical and subtropical coasts are fringed with forests which grow right down to the sea, so that the roots and lower branches of their trees are submerged at high tide. These forests, and their 'paddling trees', are called mangroves. They span sea and land and support a rich variety of wildlife from both: fish swim round their roots, monkeys live in their branches and bats pollinate their flowers.

Mangrove trees grow as high as 30 m (100 ft) and the forests form bands as wide as 20 km (12 miles). They are vital to the survival of other habitats: many animals from the open sea spend part of their lives in the mangroves, and nutrients from the forests help to nourish coral reefs. The destruction of mangroves has far-reaching effects.

## Life in the mangroves

THERE ARE 80 OR SO SPECIES of mangrove tree, all of which are land plants that have become adapted to live in the salty, water-logged mud at the edge of the sea. They filter salt from sea water through their roots, or get rid of any excess through salt glands in their leaves. To anchor themselves, the trees have more roots than trunk and branches. They absorb oxygen through special, above-ground breathing roots, and the network formed by their root system traps mud, leaves and other debris. These are a rich food supply for animals like crabs at low tide, and fish at high tide when the roots are a refuge from predators.

The mangroves recycle the nutrients in the mud. They absorb them through their roots and use them to build leaves which eventually fall, feed the mangrove animals and so give the nutrients back to the mud.

**Mangrove roots**

Mangroves have roots that spread sideways, and not straight down, so that they can stand up in soft mud. And, in order to take in oxygen, they have breathing roots that are exposed to the air. Their root systems take many different forms.

Pencil roots push up above the mud from spreading roots that support the tree.

Stilt roots look like flying buttresses.

Knee roots bend above and below the mud.

**Life in a Florida mangrove forest**

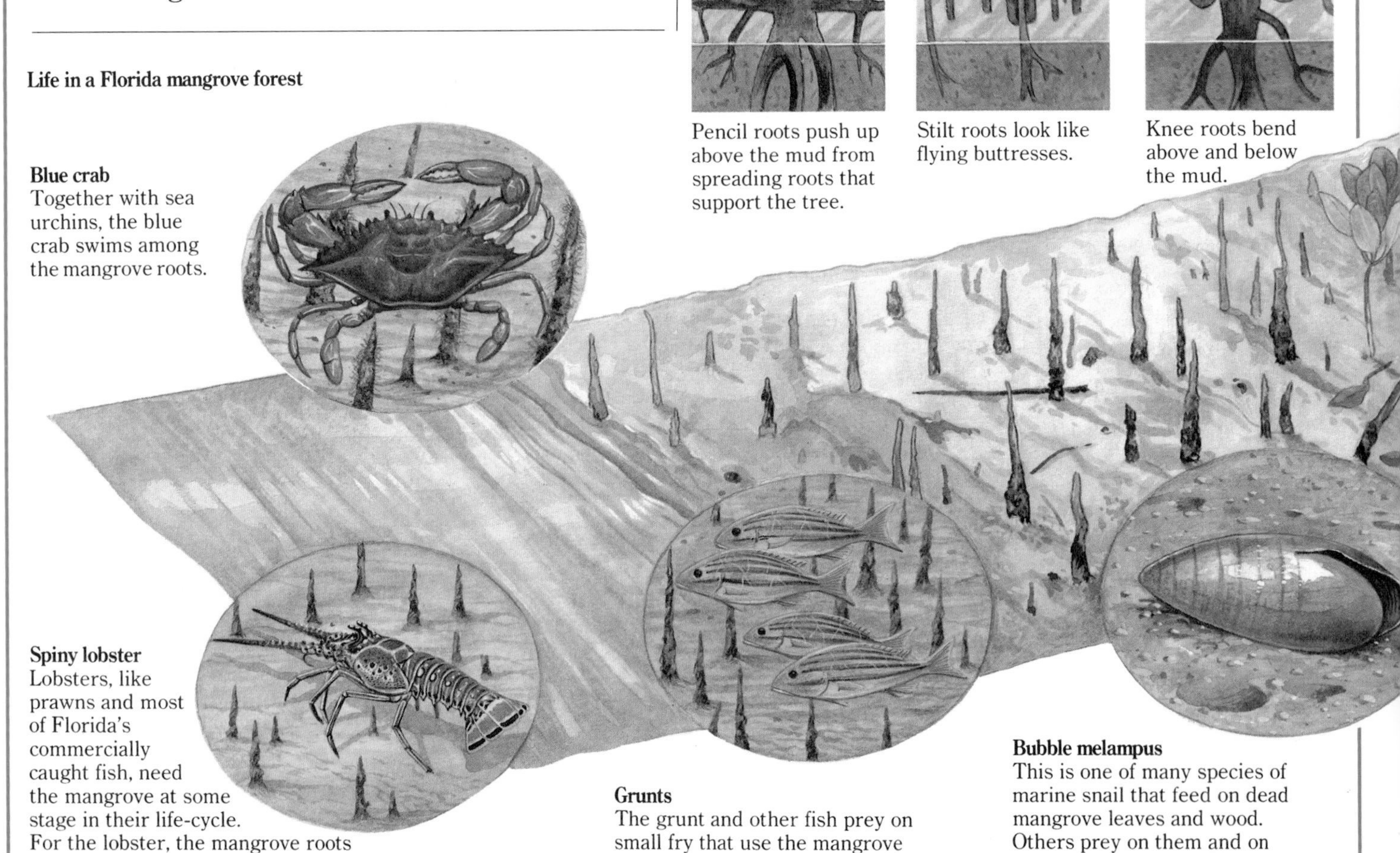

**Blue crab**
Together with sea urchins, the blue crab swims among the mangrove roots.

**Spiny lobster**
Lobsters, like prawns and most of Florida's commercially caught fish, need the mangrove at some stage in their life-cycle. For the lobster, the mangrove roots are a gathering-place prior to spawning.

**Grunts**
The grunt and other fish prey on small fry that use the mangrove roots as a nursery.

**Bubble melampus**
This is one of many species of marine snail that feed on dead mangrove leaves and wood. Others prey on them and on oysters that cling to the roots.

**Tri-coloured heron**
Birds like this heron feed in the mangroves and nest in the trees' topmost branches. In Asia and Africa, monkeys also live in the forests.

**Mangrove cuckoo**
This bird lives only in the mangroves, feeding on the huge number of insects in the forest.

**Mangrove tree crab**
Many crabs live almost entirely in trees. The mangrove tree crab climbs among the branches and drops into the water to escape danger.

**Diamond-back terrapin**
The diamond-back terrapin eats worms and snails that live in the water.

**Fiddler crab**
This crab is common to all mangroves. The male's big, bright claw attracts females and is a signal to other males to keep off.

# Wasted mangroves

MANGROVES ARE VITAL to the survival of many populations of fish that are valuable food sources for humans. They also protect coasts from storm damage, and provide a variety of useful products from medicines to animal foods.

Despite this, mangroves are regarded as useless. All over the world they are destroyed to make space for the houses, farms and factories required by growing coastal populations. But the mangroves are far more valuable than these new developments, as some countries discovered when they had to build expensive sea-defences in place of the protective coastal forest.

Scientists are beginning to show that mangroves can produce more fish, crabs, prawns, fruits, vegetables and wood, over many years, than the fish-ponds and paddy fields that replace them. If this natural power of the mangroves was used, their wildlife could be left intact.

**This Colombian mangrove forest has been cleared to make room for a new road. It is just one of many mangroves that are being destroyed worldwide.**

**WILDSIDE WATCH**

**All over the world, mangroves are being converted to different uses:**
- **Fish, prawn and crab-raising ponds in the Phillipines, Ecuador and Singapore.**
- **Rice paddies in India and Bangladesh.**
- **Housing and holiday developments in Australia, New Zealand and Florida in the United States.**
- **Wood chips and wood pulp all over south-east Asia.**

**What you can do:**
- **Spread the word! Tell people how important mangroves are to wildlife, fisheries and coastal protection.**
- **Write to your government representative and ask for help in conserving mangroves.**

# Sea meadows

IN SHALLOW COASTAL waters everywhere except in the harsh polar seas, fields of flat green blades wave in the current. They are sea grasses, true land plants that have adapted to life in the ocean. Their flattened leaves are 1 cm (½ in) wide, broad enough to slow down the water currents so that their beds become traps for sand and silt.

These sea-grass meadows are very productive and provide food and havens for many plants and animals. The richest are in the tropics. Around the Indian Ocean they feed one of the world's most threatened mammals: the dugong.

## Grazers in the meadow

DUGONGS ARE ALSO KNOWN as sea cows. In fact, they are more like sea pigs because, like pigs, they forage with their blunt snouts. They push them through mud and sand to feed on the starchy roots of sea grasses. They are the only truly marine herbivorous mammals. Dugongs are found along the coasts of the Indian and western Pacific oceans, in warm shallow bays where sea grasses grow.

In many areas their numbers are going down, mainly because they are hunted for their meat. They taste good and an adult weighs 300–400 kg (660–880 lb). In addition, their preference for coastal waters brings them into contact with human activities and they suffer oil and industrial pollution, and are disturbed by boats and entrapped in fishing nets.

Dredging and mining, which threaten to destroy the sea-grass beds themselves, are a growing threat.

**Above right: Dugongs have always been hunted for their meat, skin and oil. Today, power-boats and guns replace traditional hunting methods.**

## Sea-meadow life

SEA-GRASS BEDS are important habitats all over the world. The leaves of the grasses are home to more than 113 different species of algae, plus shrimps, snails and small squids. They also provide shelter for young fish and prawns; in the tropics these are food for large numbers of fish who travel from coral reefs to prey on them.

Dead and decaying sea grass is food for many species, but few eat the living plants. The dugong and the rare green turtle are the only large grazers in the sea meadows.

**Right: The green turtles who feed on sea grass throughout the tropics are an endangered species. Eggs are sold for food and adults are killed for their meat and shells, and to be made into leather.**
**Far right: Sea-grass meadows support a rich variety of life like this cuttlefish in the Arabian Gulf, camouflaged and waiting for passing prey.**

# and sea cows

## Fast growing, fast breathing

SEA GRASSES SPREAD over large areas by growing stems under the sand and silt. But they also flower and, like true land plants, can make seeds from which more grasses grow.

All plants generate oxygen as they grow, and, because sea grasses grow fast, they make a great deal of it: a square metre (square yard) of tropical sea grasses can create twice as much oxygen as the same area of forest. In addition to food and shelter, animals in the sea-grass beds also get plenty of oxygen to breathe.

A sea grass known as eel grass grows on colder coasts. At low tide it is grazed by wildfowl like these Brent geese.

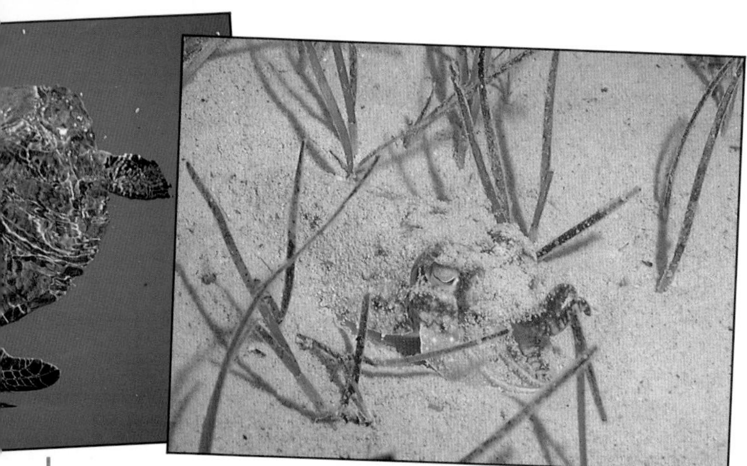

### WILDSIDE WATCH

**The dugong and its relatives, the West Indian manatee, West African manatee and Amazonian manatee are vulnerable to extinction, and threatened by hunting and entrapment in fishing nets, and by boats.**

- **If you go on holiday to Florida, take great care with your boat and fishing gear – these kill over 100 Florida manatees (a form of West Indian manatee) every year.**
- **Join a conservation organisation to help protect marine life in your country from these and similar threats.**

# Green fields in the water

LIFE ON EARTH depends on plants. They are the only living things that can trap the sun's energy to build their bodies, which in turn become food for animals.

Although they obey the same principle, the plants of the open sea are quite different from those of the land or the seaweeds of the coast. They are called phytoplankton, and are single-celled plants fractions of a millimetre across. Plankton grow best where there is a good supply of light and nutrients – especially nitrogen, found either in shallow coastal waters or brought to the surface by upwelling currents. They can multiply very rapidly and produce huge blooms that feed a host of other animals.

## Marine network of life

THESE TINY PLANTS, the phytoplankton, have their own herds of tiny herbivores and carnivores, called zooplankton. Together they drift with the ocean currents.

The zooplankton is made up of a huge range of animals, including the tiny larval stages of many much larger sea creatures, such as crabs and fish. Some feed on phytoplankton, some on other zooplankton. Adult fish and squid also feed on zooplankton and may even cannibalise young of their own kind. In turn, they feed birds and mammals.

Some very large creatures, such as whale sharks, basking sharks and manta rays feed directly on plankton. Marine food webs are therefore very complicated, and the effect of removing one link is almost impossible to predict.

In temperate and polar seas, the cold and dark limit phytoplankton growth to the summer months, and the animals that depend on it time their breeding to coincide with the seasonal bonanza. In nutrient-rich waters, big, fast-growing phytoplankton species do best, but in nutrient-poor waters small size and slow growth are the better strategies. On coral reefs, which grow in waters low in nitrogen, tiny phytoplankton take nitrogen from the air dissolved in the sea.

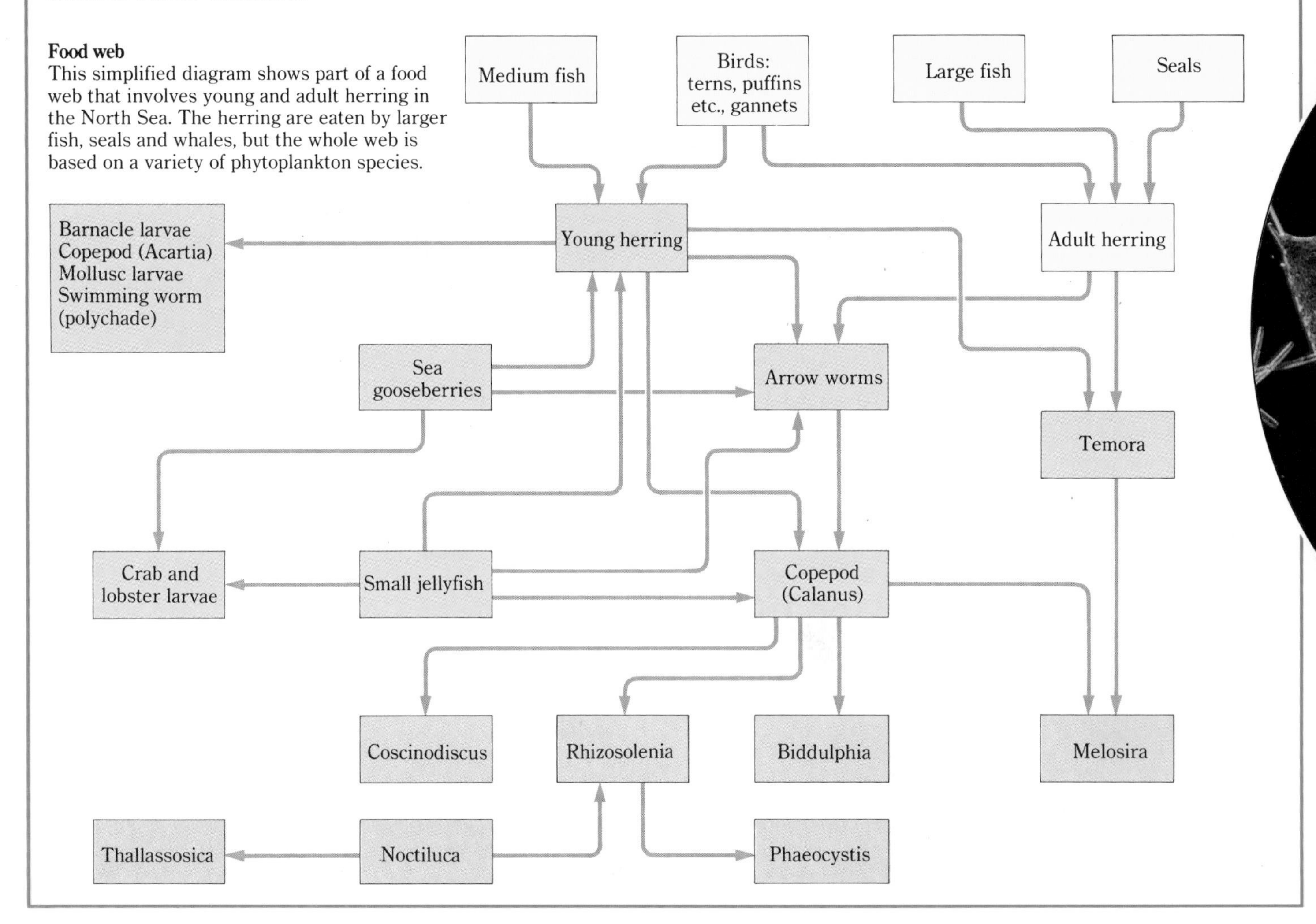


**Food web**
This simplified diagram shows part of a food web that involves young and adult herring in the North Sea. The herring are eaten by larger fish, seals and whales, but the whole web is based on a variety of phytoplankton species.

# Red blooms of death

SEWAGE AND FARM FERTILISERS in the sea can provide phytoplankton with so much nutrient that their populations explode and suffocate other sea life when their decaying bodies remove oxygen from the water. Some species of plankton are poisonous and large blooms of these are especially deadly. They often have a reddish colour, are known as 'red tides', and there is evidence to suggest that they are more frequent in modern polluted seas.

Plankton blooms can be deadly, stealing the water's oxygen so that other creatures suffocate, or producing toxins that poison marine life.

Top: Tiny animals (here magnified) graze the plant plankton and eat each other. Many are the larvae of shore-living species like crabs and barnacles. Above: Plant plankton must stay in the upper, sunlit water and, because there is nothing to anchor themselves to, they must be small enough to float and survive the buffeting of the waves. These plankton are magnified.

**WILDSIDE WATCH**

**Phytoplankton are at risk from the greenhouse effect.**

- **Even a 1°C (2°F) rise in sea temperatures could change ocean currents and the pattern of phytoplankton growth all over the world.**
- **Marine animals would be affected as a result, and fisheries could collapse.**
- **Human beings could have less oxygen to breathe - phytoplankton keep the amount in the atmosphere topped up.**

**What you can do:**

- **Save fuel in order to reduce the burning of fossil fuels which creates the greenhouse effect.**
- **For the same reason, switch off electric lights when you don't need them.**
- **And walk or cycle instead of taking a car.**
- **Write to your government representative and ask for action *now* to halt the greenhouse effect.**

# Inland sea

THE MEDITERRANEAN IS a landlocked sea. Its only connection with the world's other oceans is at the strait of Gibraltar between Europe and Africa, where the cold Atlantic water flows in. However, the effect of this cold water on the warm Mediterranean is limited: the strait is narrow – just 18 km (11 miles) wide, and the waters of the sea are held in a giant, basin-shaped depression.

Its isolation, combined with the warmth of its waters, has given the Mediterranean a rich and varied marine life. But it has also created problems. Because the sea is surrounded by land, 20 different countries fish and pollute its waters and build on its coast.

## The dustbin sea

ALTHOUGH THE PEOPLE of the Mediterranean have for centuries used its waters as a plentiful source of food and as a dumping ground for their rubbish, they affected marine life very little. All this changed in the middle of the twentieth century, when the coastal population began to soar and tourism became big business.

Now, over 100 million people live by its shores, which are visited by close on 100 million more people every summer. Eighty-five per cent of their domestic waste, including sewage, goes straight into the sea.

Industrial pollution from factories, and more than two million tonnes of crude oil spilled from tankers add to the poisonous mix, as do heavy metals, pesticides and other chemicals.

Pollution, combined with overfishing brought about by the use of small-mesh nets and even dynamiting fish populations, has made some areas of the Mediterranean into dead marine deserts.

Studies have predicted that the coastal population will reach 230 million by the year 2030. Unless strong measures are taken the problems facing this sea can only get worse.

## The decline of a rare monk

THE MEDITERRANEAN MONK SEAL is one of the world's rarest animals: there are only 500–1000 left. Hunted to the brink of extinction last century, tourism and the fishing industry are now causing another decline in the seal's population.

Many seals are drowned in fishing nets, and others are actually shot by fishermen who see them as competitors for their livelihood. But, despite that, the monk seal's biggest problem is caused by the sheer numbers of tourists and hotels that cover the coastline. The beaches where they once bred are now too crowded, and few pups have been seen in recent years. Tourist disturbance, as well as chemical pollution, could be damaging the seals' ability to have young.

**Right: One of the three species of monk seal is already extinct. Of the two that are left, the Mediterranean monk seal is the most threatened.**

**Left: This is what the entire Mediterranean Sea should look like: clear water teeming with a variety of life.**
**Above: This is what much of the Mediterranean does look like: a dead sea that has been killed by pollution and overfishing.**

# Gulls in competition

AUDOUIN'S GULL, which is unique to the Mediterranean, has been exploited by both people and other birds. Populations were reduced over the centuries when its eggs were collected for making cakes and pastry. Now, despite protection of the Audouins' most important breeding ground, large numbers of herring gulls are preventing their recovery by eating both the eggs and the chicks.

Herring gulls have become more numerous because they also feed on human refuse, which their rivals stay clear of. To add to the problem, the Audouins' own preferred diet of fish is becoming depleted through overfishing and pollution.

**Audouin's gull is one of two gull species to be classified as 'in danger of extinction'.**

**WILDSIDE WATCH**

**Conditions in some parts of the Mediterranean are so bad that people and governments have begun to take action, including the signing, in 1990, of the Nicosia Charter, which put forward a number of proposals:**

- **Sewage treatment plants for all large towns.**
- **Prevention of oil pollution by tanker ships.**
- **Protection of coastal and marine habitats and rare species.**
- **You can help too: if you live in the Mediterranean find out what your government is doing to turn the Nicosia Charter into action.**
- **Remember, the people of the Mediterranean need pollution-free seas and coastlines as much as the animals do, to support their fishing and tourist industries.**

# Forests of coral

CORAL REEFS are a mosaic made up of every colour and shape imaginable, like a rainbow come to life. They are the richest and oldest habitats on Earth, home to perhaps millions of different species of fish, invertebrate and plant. The thousands of kilometres of reef around the world are formed from the limestone skeletons of colonies of tiny animals, known as stony coral polyps, which are close relatives of sea anemones. Like the trees in a rainforest, the coral colonies are home for a host of other plants and animals that together make up a reef.

## Inhabitants of the coral reef

REEF-BUILDING STONY CORALS have been growing in shallow tropical seas for 45 million years or more, while the coral reefs that we see in the world today started developing about 10,000 years ago. This long period of growth has given corals, and all the animals and plants that inhabit the reef, time to evolve a dazzling range of forms, colours and lifestyles.

For example, a single coral colony can support 16 different species of fish and crustaceans, such as crabs and shrimps, and perhaps 103 different species of worm. Storms help to keep up the variety too: by destroying coral heads they make room for new colonists. Nutrients are recycled through all the reef's inhabitants so that nothing is wasted: the reef's abundant life can only thrive in waters that are not over-rich in nutrients.

**Right: Different shapes of stony coral are suited to different parts of the reef: branching corals in shallow water, 'brain' ones in deeper water. Soft corals lack stony skeletons and form branching fingers. Bright red seaweeds thrive in the roughest waves and protect the reef from damage.**

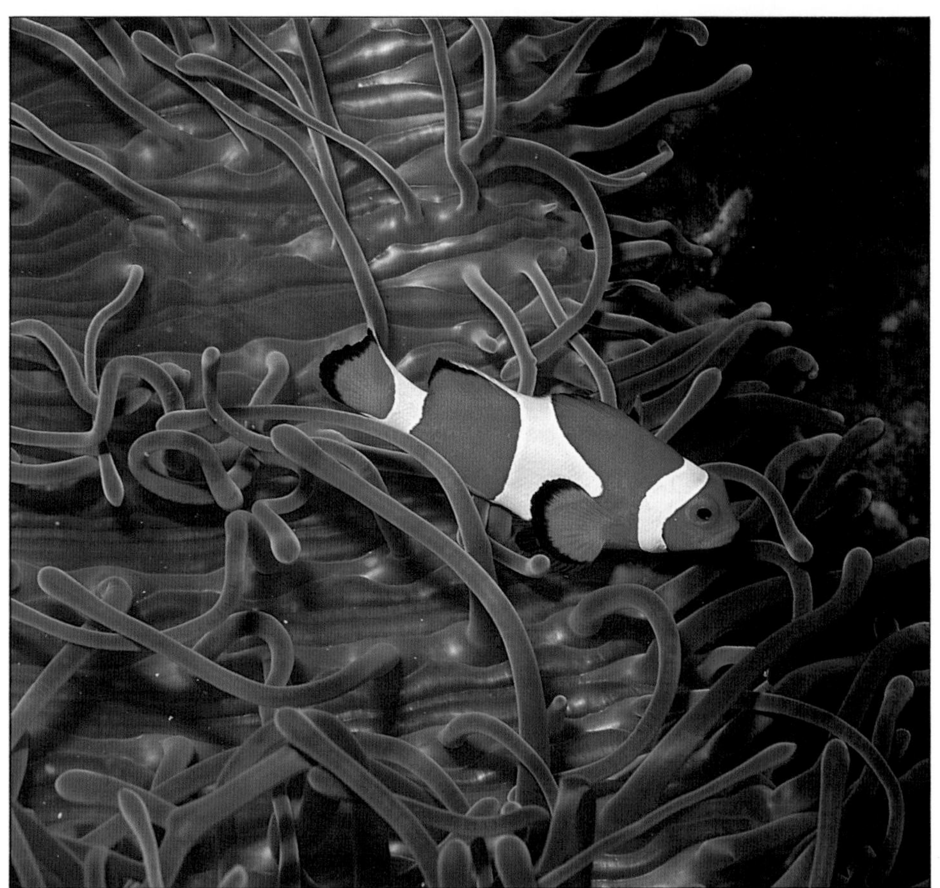

**Above: Reef relationships are complex and bizarre. This clown fish is immune to the stinging tentacles of its anemone home, where it is safe from predators. A single large female dominates the males in an anemone, but if she dies the largest male turns into a female to replace her.**

**Left: Sea fans are also corals, but their skeletons are horny and not stony. They grow in the deeper, darker parts of the reef.**

**Right: This sea slug from Australia's Great Barrier Reef feeds on algae. Like many other sea slugs, its bright colours warn potential predators that it is poisonous.**

# Reefs need corals, corals need plants

AS COLONIES OF stony or hard coral polyps grow, their limestone skeletons become enlarged too. Polyps filter food from the water by using their tentacles, but the extra energy that corals need in order to build their limestone skeletons comes from tiny algal plants that are in the polyps' bodies.

The algae need light and warmth to flourish, so reef-building corals can only live in clear water, less than 30 m (100 ft) deep, that is never cooler than 20°C (68°F).

This close-up of a single, stony coral polyp shows the tiny algal plants inside.

## WILDSIDE WATCH

**Reef-forming stony corals grow at the rate of just a few centimetres or even millimetres a year: single branches of some colonies may take centuries to grow. So you can see how important it is that the reefs are protected – now!**

- **Spread the word! People know that tropical rainforests are important and threatened, but they don't know about coral reefs.**
- **If you visit a reef, just look – don't touch or break the corals and don't take anything away with you.**

# Raiders of the reef

STORMS AND HURRICANES increase the diversity of coral reefs by creating new habitats, but man-made problems are destroying the stable environment on which they depend. Silt may be deposited in once-clear waters. Sewage pollution may increase nutrient levels so that seaweed proliferates and smothers the corals. And now there is an additional threat: that corals may not be able to keep up with the rising sea levels caused by the greenhouse effect.

## Captive jewels

THE JEWEL-LIKE COLOURS of reef inhabitants make them very popular with amateur aquarists. Over two million coral fish are imported into the United States every year from the Philippines alone, and millions more are taken from reefs elsewhere to end up in fish tanks worldwide. Over 60 per cent die in the first six months of captivity.

Numbers of popular species of fish are falling due to over-gathering and the delicate balance of many reefs is being disrupted.

**Above: Many species of reef fish that are caught for aquaria can feed only on living coral. As a result, they die in captivity.**
**Right: A butterfly fish in its natural habitat.**

# A plague of thorns

SINCE THE 1960s Australia's Great Barrier Reef and other reefs around the Pacific have been threatened by population explosions of the coral-eating crown of thorns starfish. Up to 45 cm (18 in) across, a single crown of thorns can eat a patch of coral half its size in a night. It digests the polyps by turning its stomach inside out, leaving behind a dead, white skeleton. In this way, a whole coral colony can be destroyed in just a few nights.

Scientists are still finding out exactly why these plagues happen but the reasons include over-collecting of crown of thorns predators, such as triton shells, and the gathering of reef fish that eat the larvae.

**Scientists don't know where the crown of thorns starfish comes from, or why it infests and devours coral reefs around the Pacific.**

# Dredging and mining

IN MANY POOR countries the limestone of the reef is the cheapest available building material. Huge areas of reef are mined and show few signs of recovery even after 20 years. The coral rock is often used to build coastal walls as protection from rough seas, but the best protection is the reef itself.

Silt is another big reef killer. It smothers corals and clouds the water, cutting out light. Human activities, on land as well as in the sea, generate silt: felling forests allows soil to wash away down rivers into the sea; transporting the logs from the forest means digging new roads; and exporting the wood entails building a harbour for ships by dredging sand and mud from the sea bed.

**Reefs are often destroyed and used as building bricks, while coastal development creates silt that smothers and kills coral.**

# Coral decorations

A COLLECTION OF exquisite tropical shells on a shelf, a branch of centuries-old coral skeleton in a glass case, a pearly clam shell holding soap in the bathroom. All are the dead remains of animals taken in their thousands from coral reefs for sale as decorations. Trade in many corals and shells is illegal but they still find their way into shops in tourist resorts and modern cities.

**Divers collect live animals, which are killed to provide the dead, dry shells sold all over the world.**

## WILDSIDE WATCH

**What can be done to help save coral reefs?**

- **Educate people about the value of the reefs in their country, and how they can benefit from caring for them.**
- **Create marine parks with areas that people can visit to learn about reefs – and areas where no one can go.**
- **Control the trade in live and dead coral reefs and invertebrates. Encourage captive breeding of reef animals so that they are not taken from the wild.**

**What you can do:**

- **Never buy dead corals or tropical shells, and tell your friends not to.**

# Treasure islands

ISLANDS ARE SPRINKLED throughout the world's oceans. They may be very large chunks of land mass that have broken away from a continent; they may be small, coral atolls; or they may be ancient volcanoes. But they all have one feature in common: isolation. Species on islands are isolated from the competition and predators of the mainland, and evolve along unique lines. This gives rise to animals and plants that are found nowhere else on Earth, called endemic species.

## Breaking into paradise

ISLAND ECOSYSTEMS are very fragile. Any change in the special conditions in which island life evolves, such as the introduction of species, can cause a complete collapse in the delicate balance of island life.

The island of Mauritius and its collection of surrounding islets in the Indian Ocean were once home to many endemic plants and animals. However, introduced goats and rabbits grazed plants and reduced shelter for animals, and introduced rats killed reptiles and birds. Many species were wiped out, but some survived on tiny Round Island which, just by chance, escaped colonisation by the rats.

**Round Island animals and plants**

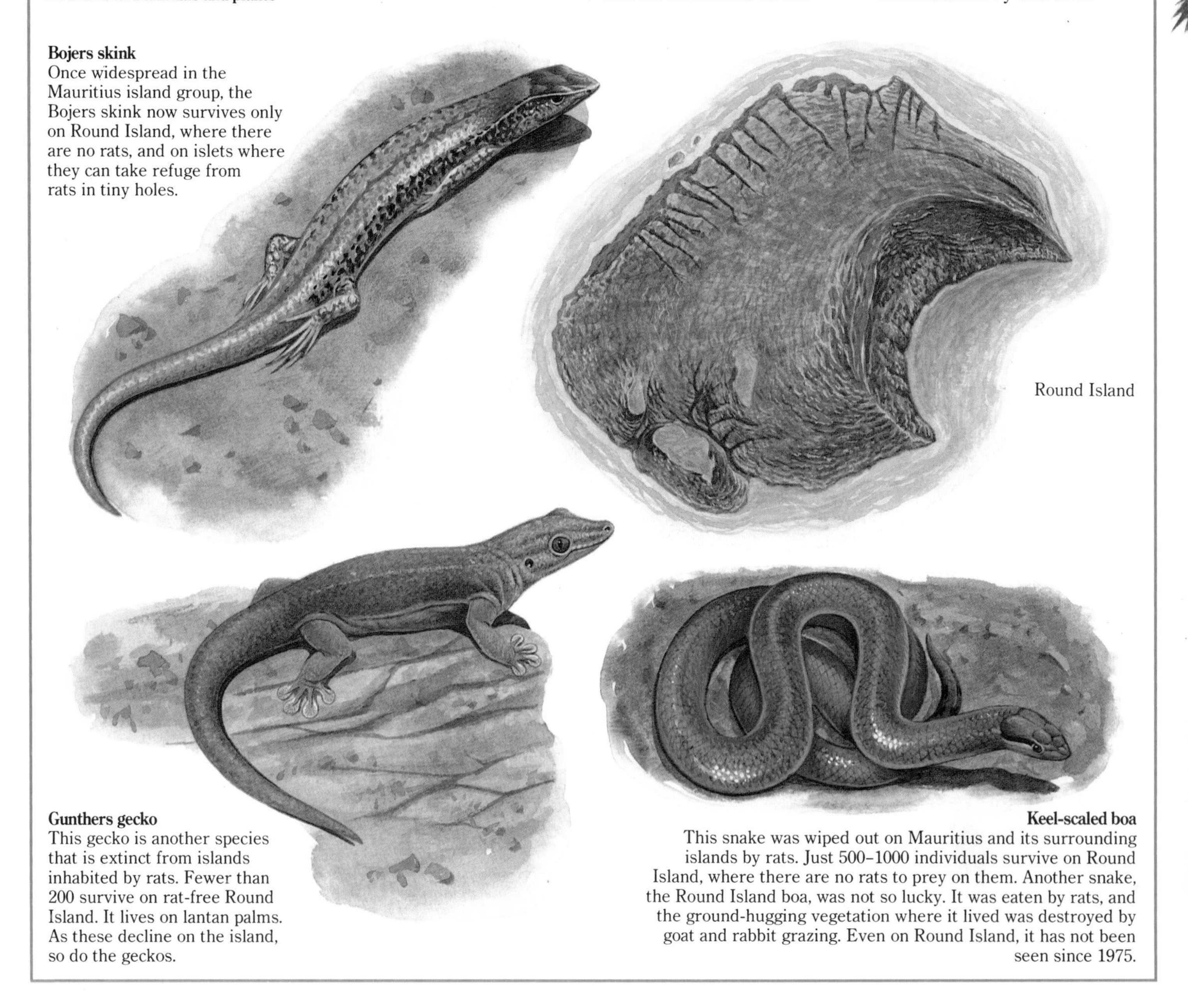

**Bojers skink**
Once widespread in the Mauritius island group, the Bojers skink now survives only on Round Island, where there are no rats, and on islets where they can take refuge from rats in tiny holes.

Round Island

**Gunthers gecko**
This gecko is another species that is extinct from islands inhabited by rats. Fewer than 200 survive on rat-free Round Island. It lives on lantan palms. As these decline on the island, so do the geckos.

**Keel-scaled boa**
This snake was wiped out on Mauritius and its surrounding islands by rats. Just 500–1000 individuals survive on Round Island, where there are no rats to prey on them. Another snake, the Round Island boa, was not so lucky. It was eaten by rats, and the ground-hugging vegetation where it lived was destroyed by goat and rabbit grazing. Even on Round Island, it has not been seen since 1975.

**Round Island survivors**
These palms were wiped out on many islands and threatened on Round Island by forest clearance and goat and rabbit grazing. Soil erosion caused by earlier over-grazing is preventing the growth of young palms, even though goats and rabbits have been removed. Only one hurricane palm still stood in 1982.

# Islands of evolution

THE GALAPAGOS ISLANDS, found 800 km (500 miles) to the west of Ecuador in the Pacific Ocean, have never been part of the mainland. They were formed by volcanic action during the last million years, which is quite a short time in evolutionary terms. Despite this, the few animals and plants that arrived on the Galapagos originally, drifting in the sea or blown by the wind, have evolved into many different species unique to the islands. It was this uniqueness that struck the young Charles Darwin when he visited the islands and helped him to formulate his theory of evolution.

Sadly, the beautiful and biologically important natural history of the Galapagos is now threatened. More people visit the islands each year, (44,000 in 1989), causing sewage pollution, increased erosion and disturbance, and the introduction of rats, cats and dogs from tourist boats. Turtles, sea lions and sharks are killed in nets set illegally to catch smaller fish.

**The giant tortoises that are unique to the Galapagos exist in different forms on each of the 13 main islands. Nineteenth-century seamen killed them for meat, introduced goats destroyed their habitat and rats ate their young. Today, they are protected by law and bred in captivity on the islands.**

**WILDSIDE WATCH**

**Island species are still disappearing, before scientists can find out more about them.**

- **If you visit an island, show respect for its wildlife: a large proportion of the world's endangered species is unique to islands.**
- **Be careful not to let your pets or domestic animals escape if you visit an island with them. They can damage the island's native wildlife.**
- **Join an organisation such as the World Wide Fund for Nature (WWFN) which campaigns for the conservation of island species throughout the world.**

# Ocean wanderers

Life-cycle of the Pacific salmon

SWIMMING IS A CHEAP form of travel. Swimming animals use less energy per distance covered than those that fly or run. And animals in the sea can cut journey costs even more by making use of ocean currents. So marine animals can undertake long journeys across vast stretches of water, making use of resources in different locations at different times in their breeding and life cycle.

There is a disadvantage to all this ocean wandering, however, which is that at almost every stage of the journey a new set of predators – both animal and human – is waiting.

**8 Home to spawn**
Adult salmon return to their home river and swim upstream. They are food for bears, gulls and other animals, and many are caught by humans as they come to the coast.

**7 Out at sea**
Fish roam, feeding and growing, for 18 months or more depending on species. They are preyed on by seals, sea lions, dolphins and killer whales, and entrapped by nets in the mid-Pacific.

## Swimming for their life

IN STREAMS AND RIVERS along the northern coast of the Pacific, from Hokkaido to Oregon, seven species of salmon lay their eggs.

Rivers offer protection for the young fish, but only the sea can provide the abundance of food that they need in order to grow to adulthood. So, they leave the rivers and wander the Pacific, feeding and growing, only returning to the stream where they hatched to spawn and die.

The numbers of fish involved are astronomical and they form a cornerstone of Pacific marine and coastal ecology, eating and in turn being eaten by other predators. But now their numbers could be falling as human activities at sea, on the coast and up river put pressure on every stage in their life cycle.

**Three Pacific salmon**

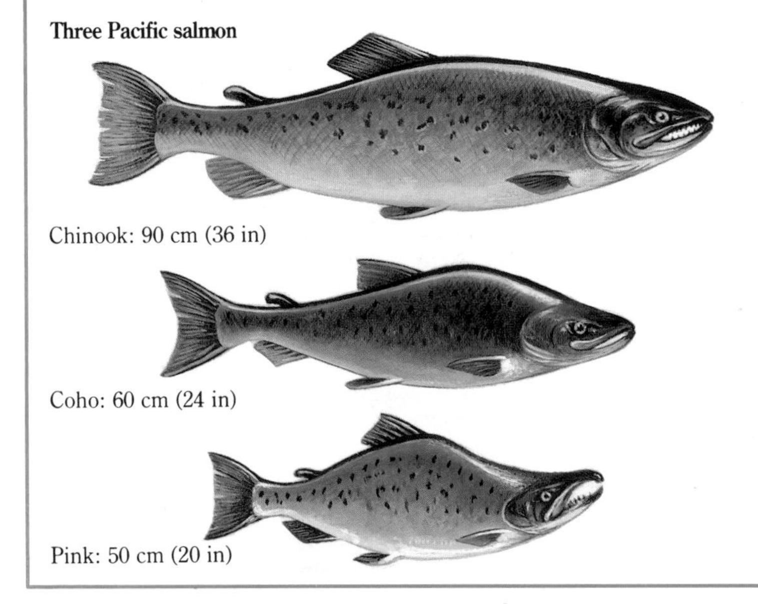

Chinook: 90 cm (36 in)

Coho: 60 cm (24 in)

Pink: 50 cm (20 in)

**6 Dams and wetland destruction**
Humans need water for irrigation schemes and hydro-electric power. Dams block the salmon migration, and some rivers have too little water left to sustain spawning salmon.

**1 Spawning and adults' death**
Male and female salmon spawn in a gravel scrape, then die, their task complete. Their bodies help to fertilise the river, and nourish their eggs and young fish.

**2 Eggs and aelvin**
Eggs hatch into aelvin (tiny fish) in 50–100 days. Many are eaten by numerous natural predators.

**3 Fry**
Young fish wriggle out of the gravel and are swept downstream. The time they spend in the river before going to sea varies from species to species.

**4 Logging**
Deforestation around spawning rivers reduces shade so that the water gets too hot for salmon to spawn. It also increases erosion, and silt that enters the water as a result may suffocate eggs and fry.

**5 Salmon farming**
Farmed salmon kept in pens in rivers may breed with wild ones. The young they produce are poor survivors.

# Miniature voyagers

MANY MARINE ANIMALS are permanently attached to rocks, seaweed or sand. If conditions become unfavourable they cannot move to another location. To combat this, a large number produce tiny, free-swimming offspring (larvae) that can drift in plankton for weeks, travelling perhaps thousands of kilometres before settling down.

If pollution strikes a sea shore, the planktonic larvae can escape and recolonise a different area. Even so, severe pollution, particularly by chemicals in the sea, can cause death and deformity before larvae have a chance to 'emigrate'.

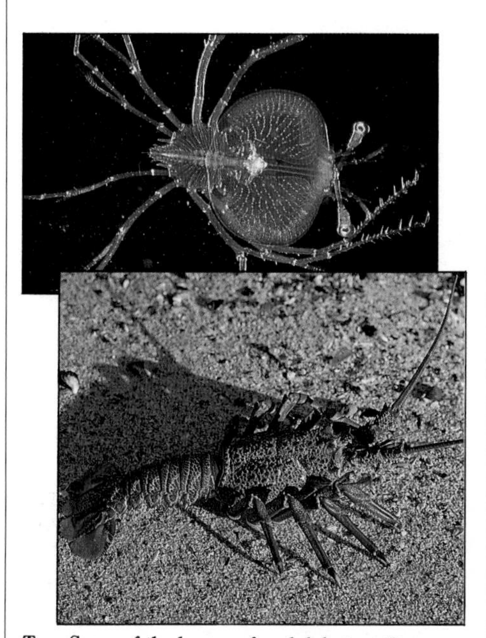

**Top: Some of the larvae of rock lobsters that spawn in western Australia drift in ocean currents to the east coast of Africa where they settle down to adult life (above).**

**WILDSIDE WATCH**

**Travelling can be dangerous for ocean wanderers.**
- **North Atlantic plaice spawn in the Wadden See off the Dutch coast and catch a north-going current up into the North Sea to feed and grow. Pollution threatens the young on the spawning grounds; adults suffer from overfishing.**

**What you can do:**
- **Join a conservation organisation that fights marine pollution, to help protect all sea life.**

# Fishing for trouble

EVERY YEAR, 60 million tonnes of fish are taken from the oceans of the world using a variety of fishing methods. Fishing is quite different from growing crops or raising animals for food, because it is really a form of hunting, and the fish we catch and eat are wild animals. We can count fields of wheat or cows, and know how to control their environment to produce more or less grain and beef. But we don't know exactly what makes the numbers of wild fish grow or shrink, or even how many there are. Yet we expect to be able to go on catching ever-bigger hauls without understanding what this is doing to fish populations and other animals that depend on them.

**Puffins and sand eels**
In the Shetland Islands off the north coast of Scotland, whole puffin colonies failed to breed in the late 1980s. This was because their favourite food, the sand eel, disappeared after a huge increase in the sand-eel catch for use as fish meal.

**Dolphins and anchovetta**
The Humboldt current off Peru nourished huge populations of anchovetta until the 1970s, when changes in ocean currents caused them to crash. Fishermen needed a new type of catch and turned to dusky dolphins – 10,000 of them a year.

# Overfishing

PEOPLE HAVE ALWAYS caught sea fish, but for thousands of years this had little effect on fish populations because fishing methods were too inefficient to catch huge numbers. But in the last 100 years, and especially in the last 50, fishing has become so technologically advanced that fish have little chance of escape.

These days, large engine-powered boats can reach the remotest parts of the world in search of fish. Not only that – stronger, bigger nets of man-made fibre have been developed and can stretch for kilometres across the sea and down to the ocean floor, covering an enormous area.

Underwater sonar is another modern tool that has come into its own, allowing shoals of fish to be located exactly. But high-tech fishing costs a lot of money, making even bigger catches essential to pay for it all.

Most of the world's fisheries show signs of overfishing: the catches are smaller, and also contain smaller, younger fish. This is evidence that breeding in some areas can't replace the numbers of fish killed – a sure sign that the population is in serious difficulties.

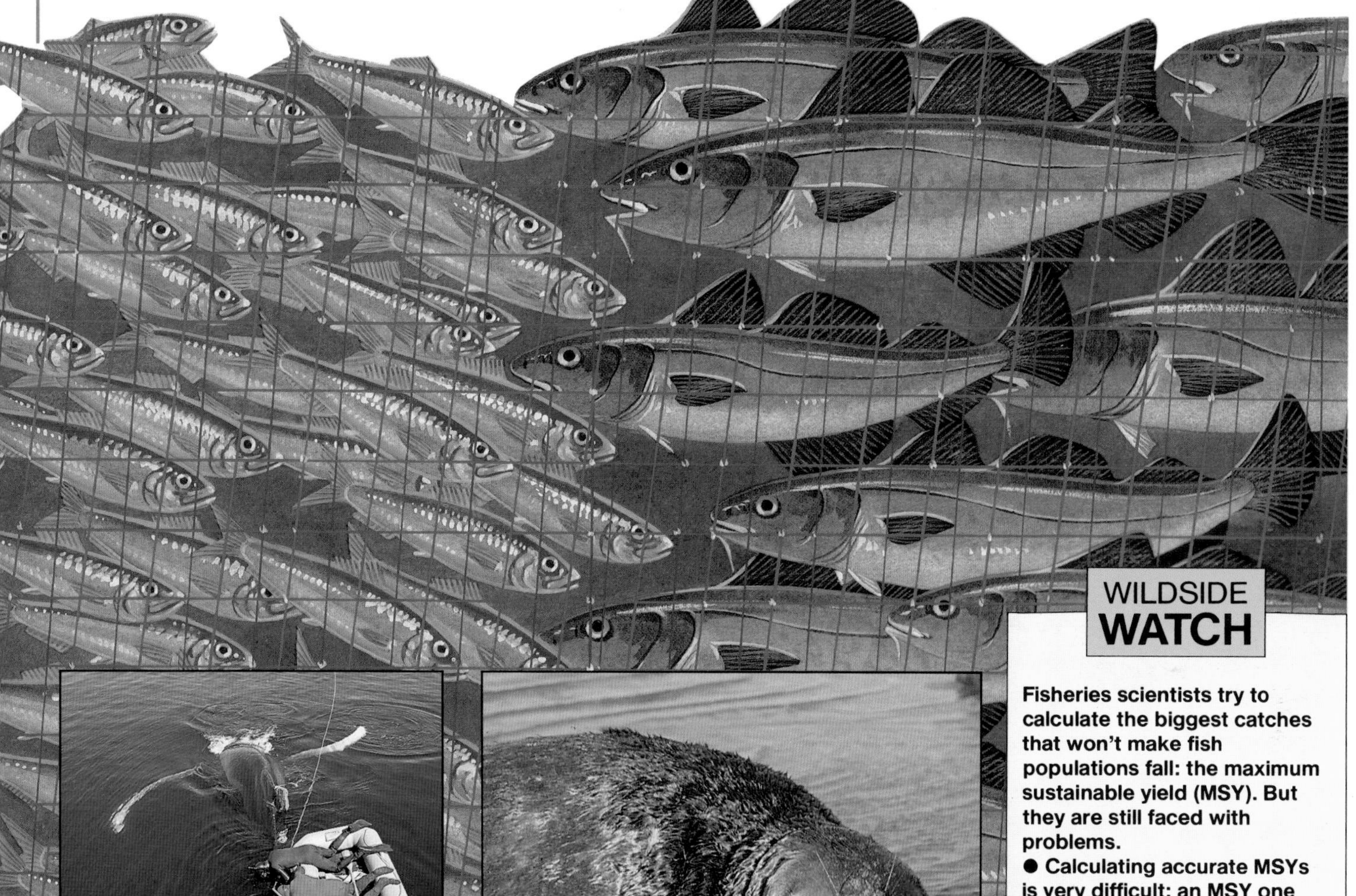

**Whales and capelin**
In the shallow sea off Newfoundland in Canada, overfishing caused the offshore capelin population to plummet in the late 1970s. When humpbacked whales moved close to shore to eat the capelin spawning there, many were entangled in fishing nets and drowned.

**Seals and cod**
Cod numbers off Canada's east coast have crashed because of over-estimation of MSYs (maximum sustainable yields) and breaking limits on catch sizes. In 1990, fishermen claimed that seals, not overfishing, were to blame and called for a cull of grey seals.

## WILDSIDE WATCH

**Fisheries scientists try to calculate the biggest catches that won't make fish populations fall: the maximum sustainable yield (MSY). But they are still faced with problems.**

- **Calculating accurate MSYs is very difficult: an MSY one year could spell disaster the next.**
- **Setting maximum permitted catches and minimum fish sizes can help populations recover. But enforcing the regulations is hard – the sea is very big and every boat can't be watched.**

**What you can do:**

- **Find out if your government has a fisheries policy that promotes conservation of fish.**
- **If it doesn't have one, ask: 'Why not?'**

# Wall of death

FISHING NETS ARE NOT selective. Even when care is taken to set them around particular shoals of fish, other species are also caught. In many cases, no such care is taken and in the quest for ever-larger catches of commercially valuable fish, other animals are killed. To catch fish that live at the bottom of the sea, a net is dragged over the sea bed churning up mud and sand and wiping out populations of worms, shellfish and other invertebrates that are vital to marine food chains.

Fewer and fewer places are safe from the damage done by thoughtless fishing. Today, high-tech equipment allows boats to venture into shallow or rocky waters where life was once safe.

## The drift to trouble

INVISIBLE AS GOSSAMER and as tough as steel, 50,000 km (30,000 miles) of driftnets stretch in sections sometimes 50 km (30 miles) long throughout the Pacific Ocean. They are set at night by a fleet of 800 boats from Japan, Korea and Taiwan to catch squid, salmon and albacore tuna, but they catch anything in their path: fish, turtles, seals, whales, dolphins, and sometimes seabirds. It is impossible to know exactly how many creatures are killed, but as many as 17,000 or more dolphins are drowned each year. Tuna and other commercially valuable species are at least used – the other bodies simply rot. Driftnets are becoming a problem all over the world. For example, 536 seabirds were taken from nets set in a single bay on the coast of south-west England.

**Sunfish**
Many large fish like this ocean sunfish take years to reach maturity – and are then killed in driftnets. How will their populations cope?

**Dolphin in net**
Driftnets set to catch squid are indiscriminate and also drown many species of dolphin. Worldwide, perhaps as many as 100,000 individuals are killed this way each year.

# Encircled by death

IN THE EASTERN tropical Pacific Ocean, yellowfin tuna follow schools of dolphins, swimming just underneath.

Fishermen have made use of this, setting purse-shaped nets around the schools. When the nets are hauled in to catch the tuna, the dolphins are crushed to death or drown. Between 120,000 and 250,000 died this way each year until people in America and Europe stopped buying tuna. Fishermen were forced to change their methods. By 1992, killing dolphins with nets could be banned by governments throughout the world.

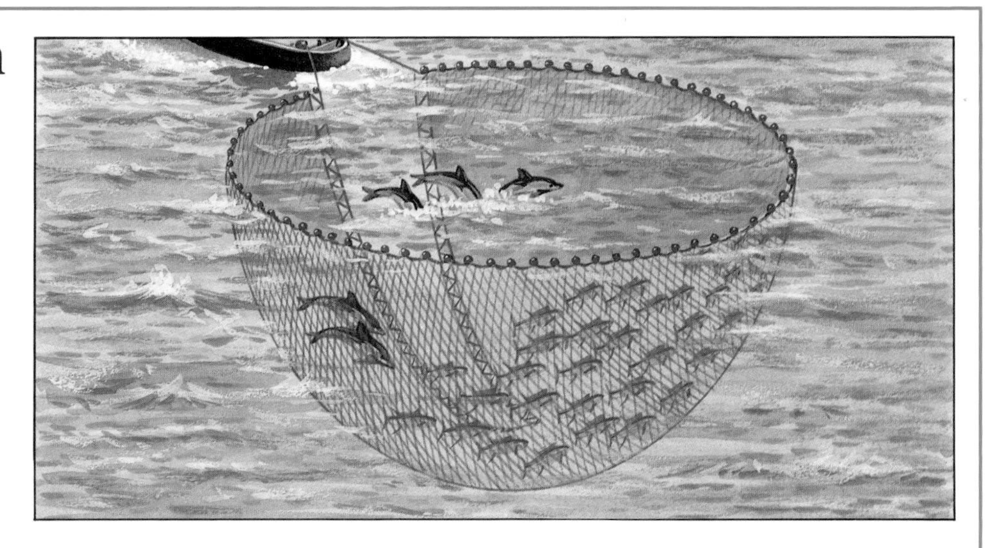

**Loggerhead turtle**
Turtles use the oceans as highways to their feeding grounds and breeding beaches. All species are endangered and driftnet deaths are an additional pressure.

## WILDSIDE WATCH

**There are ways in which dolphins and other sea creatures can be protected from indiscriminate killing.**

- **Fishermen can release dolphins caught in nets.**
- **Hooks and lines, rather than unselective driftnets, can be used to catch specific types of fish.**

**What you can do:**

- **Only buy canned fish that states on the label that it was caught in a dolphin-friendly way. Check with conservation organisations that this is correct.**

# Shark!

SHARKS ARE PERHAPS the most feared of all animals, and are usually portrayed as 'vicious killers'. But shark attacks are very rare events: you are more likely to be hit by lightning than bitten by a shark! Indeed, one of the world's best-loved animals, the elephant, is responsible for 10 times more human deaths each year than the shark. From their point of view, sharks have far more to fear from us, because for every human victim claimed by sharks, we kill four million of these magnificent creatures.

## Prey to man

HUNTING SHARKS FOR SPORT has a 'macho' image, and the sport's popularity could unbalance marine ecosystems by driving species of large predatory shark to extinction. Commercial fishing also threatens many species of shark all over the oceans. And now there is a new menace in the form of shark-fin soup, a traditional Chinese dish, which has recently become popular in other parts of the world.

Thousands of sharks are being killed to supply this growing market, and have almost disappeared from some places such as the Cocos Islands off Costa Rica, once famous for shoaling hammerhead sharks. Some species may not be able to recover from this slaughter because sharks are slow breeders; they produce just a few live young fish or large eggs at a time.

**Above: Hammerhead sharks are vanishing from tropical seas. Around the Galapagos Islands they are killed to provide fins for a new fashion in soup. Right: Many sharks die so that fishermen can have trophies and take photographs: their dead bodies are then thrown away.**

# An ancient predator

SHARKS ARE SUPREMELY well adapted to find and kill prey – they've been doing it for 300 million years after all! They can smell a drop of blood in 115 litres (230 pints) of water, sense the electrical activity from an animal's nerves, and have up to 20 rows of teeth.

Even so, only 10 per cent of the more than 370 species of shark attack humans and only a minority are fast-swimming predators. Instead, many are scavengers, and even the largest of all – the whale and basking sharks – are harmless plankton feeders.

**Sharks have always been feared because of their reputation for attacking swimmers. In fact, such attacks are extremely rare.**

The Great White. Not a horror-movie star, it is a well-adapted predator, vital to a healthy ecosystem.

# Basking in death

BASKING SHARKS are so called because they 'bask' close to the surface, filtering their plankton food from the water. Almost nothing is known about their biology and their ocean wanderings, although they appear off the British and Irish coasts in summer. There, 800 to 1000 are killed each year because their massive six-tonne bodies contain large amounts of an oil used in expensive cosmetics.

Female basking sharks may not breed until fully mature and most of those killed are large females that show signs of recent mating. So this fishery may be destroying the breeding population, and basking sharks in the waters of the north Atlantic could disappear.

**Cosmetics without cruelty**
Basking sharks are the source of a special oil used in expensive cosmetics. But if some companies can make products without this oil, others should also be able to do so. After all, who will replace an extinct species?

## WILDSIDE WATCH

**There are a number of things you can do to help sharks.**

- **Avoid shark-fin soup.**
- **Tell people how rare shark attacks really are.**
- **Don't buy cosmetics containing shark oil.**
- **Tell people that many species give birth to live young.**
- **Improve the image of sharks by telling people the important role they play as predators and scavengers in the sea.**
- **Tell people that sharks have been on Earth much longer than we have.**

# The deepest ocean

THE LARGEST PART of the world's oceans is more than 900 m (2950 ft) below the surface. Even in the clearest water no light can penetrate beyond this depth, so the deep oceans are utterly dark. They are also cold, a few degrees above freezing at 1000 m (3250 ft), and under huge pressure from the water above. The bodies and animal droppings which rain down from the sunlit surface waters are the only source of food. They sustain a surprising variety of life.

## Deep-dive experts

SPERM WHALES are deep-diving specialists. They routinely go below 800 m (2650 ft) and sometimes as far as 3000 m (10,000 ft), staying down for 50–90 minutes or more. They dive with empty lungs – all the oxygen they need is stored in their muscles – and economise further on their use of oxygen by restricting their blood flow to essential organs.

The spermaceti wax in their heads is a buoyancy control system which helps save energy. When it is warmed with blood, it is liquid and heavy so the whale sinks. When the wax is cooled with water in the animal's vast nostril, it becomes solid and light and carries the whale effortlessly to the surface.

In the cold, dark depths of the ocean sperm whales hunt squid up to 19 m (62 ft) long. They determine their position with sonar 'clicks', and use the spermaceti like a sound-focusing lens, perhaps stunning the squid with extra-powerful clicks.

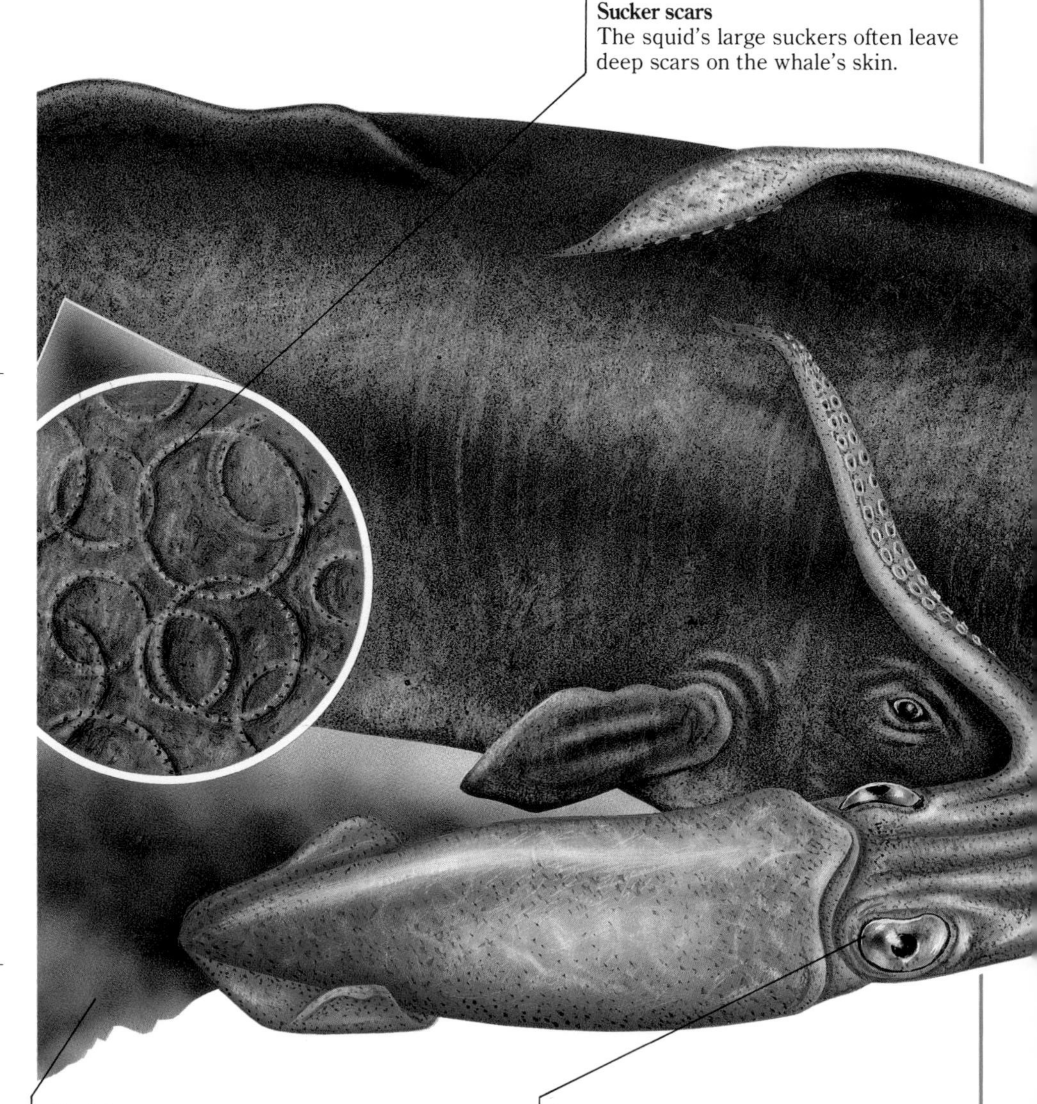

**Sucker scars**
The squid's large suckers often leave deep scars on the whale's skin.

**The ink-sac**
Nearly all squids have an ink-sac from which dark fluid can be squirted to confuse an enemy. People have actually used this ink for writing.

**Eyes**
The eye of a giant squid can be 40 cm (1 ft 6 in) across – bigger than a football. Some squids have a huge left eye and a small right eye. Others have eyes on the ends of stalks which carry their own built-in 'searchlights'.

## Life at the bottom

MANY STRANGE KINDS of invertebrates, found only in the abyssal depths, filter food from the water, and from the mud that covers much of the flat, deep-sea floor. Because food is scarce, the fish are equipped to eat anything, no matter how large, by having mouths that are huge in comparison to their bodies.

A mate may be hard to find in the dark so some creatures produce their own light to attract one. Male angler fish guarantee a partner by becoming part of the female's body.

**Deep-sea fish have enormous mouths to make the most of any food that comes their way, and produce light to signal to mates in the darkness.**

**Predator and prey**
Sperm whales, found in all the world's oceans, feed almost exclusively on squid. The bigger the whale, the bigger its prey; scientists can gauge the squid's size from the horny 'beaks' found in sperm whales' stomachs.

# Poisoning the future

GIANT TRENCHES 6000 m (19,500 ft) or more in depth are formed where two continents collide with each other, deep under the sea, forcing one down under the other. Here humans dump some of their deadliest rubbish, including highly radioactive waste packed in concrete drums. The concrete can last 600 years, but the waste may be dangerous for 10,000.

No one knows what will happen far in the future, when the drums break open, or, much sooner, if they are crushed in an earthquake.

Everything from sewage sludge to nuclear waste is taken out to sea and dropped on to the sea bed.

**Arms and tentacles**
Squids have eight arms and two tentacles that are much longer and which are usually kept folded up. But when extended to catch prey, the tentacles can be five times as long as the body. They are formidable weapons because they are covered in suckers – a giant squid may carry over a thousand of these living 'vacuum cups'.

# Riches of the deep

VALUABLE MINERALS are found in the mud and rocks that cover much of the sea floor, and people are already trying to bring them to the surface. This mining of the oceans could destroy vast areas of sea-bed ecosystem. It could also damage the recycling of nutrients on which life in the oceans' shallow waters relies.

Giant worms 3 m (10 ft) long, over a geothermal vent in the deep Galapagos trench. They get energy from bacteria in their bodies, which make use of chemicals instead of light.

**WILDSIDE WATCH**

**The abyssal plain is between 3500 m (11,500 ft) and 11,000 m (36,000 ft) below the surface of the sea. It is increasingly threatened by human activities.**

- **Find out if your government is dumping waste in the deep sea.**
- **Find out whether it has plans for deep-sea mining.**
- **If the answer to either of these questions is 'Yes', write and tell your government representative of the damage these activities can cause.**

# Sea of ice

THE NORTH POLE is in the middle of a sea that is edged by the northern margins of the American and Eurasian continents. The sea is the Arctic Ocean, which is covered all year round with a layer of ice metres thick. Life is teeming beneath the ice: plankton that grows on its underside supports a whole food chain, from tiny grazers, through fish, to seals and polar bears.

For centuries the Eskimos, or Inuits as they prefer to be called, have used and hunted this rich habitat without damaging it. In more recent times the region's oil, minerals and wildlife have been exploited purely for profit, with much harm to the wilderness.

## Bears on ice

AIR IN THE ARCTIC can fall to temperatures greatly below zero and the water is freezing, but a polar bear's thick fur and layer of fat keep it impervious to the cold. For food, the bears hunt seals, which they catch when the seals come to their breathing-holes in the ice.

Polar bears are perfectly tuned to their environment, and have difficulty in adjusting to changes in it. One such change might be brought about by the greenhouse effect, which could cause warming of the climate and the disappearance of their icy home. Pollution from oil wells and mining operations is already a threat to bears' lives, as are the increasing numbers of people visiting the Arctic in search of oil and mineral wealth: the bears seek easy meals on human rubbish dumps only to be shot as a menace.

**Above: The greenhouse effect could warm the world by about 1°C (2°F) by 2025. The Arctic's ice cover would shrink and, with it, the habitat of the polar bear.**
**Right: These polar bears are risking their lives for an easy meal at the dump; a potential threat to people, they could be shot for being too close to human habitation.**

# The most toxic whale in the world

BELUGA WHALES spend their summers in the shallow coastal waters of Canada and Greenland, on the fringes of the polar sea, and their winters at the edge of the Arctic ice. Only Eskimos hunt them, but commercial whaling in the nineteenth and early twentieth centuries so reduced their numbers that even this small-scale hunting puts their survival at risk.

In the gulf of St Lawrence, on Canada's sub-arctic east coast, pollution, not hunting, threatens the belugas. PCBs and other poisonous chemicals, dumped by factories along the banks of the St Lawrence river and its tributaries, are washed into the gulf where they concentrate in the belugas' bodies. The pollutants cause stomach ulcers and cancer, reduce the animals' ability to breed and kill at least one whale every month.

The belugas of the gulf of St Lawrence are so full of chemicals that they could be classed as illegal toxic waste. The poisons they have absorbed last for many years: the whales will go on dying, even if the pollution stops tomorrow.

# A new kind of ivory

WALRUS ARE UNIQUE to the Arctic Ocean, feeding on sea-floor shellfish and sleeping off their meal on the rocky shores. They are now threatened because an international ban on trade in elephant ivory has created a big demand for walrus tusks. At least 12,000 walrus are killed in Alaska alone each year, and scientists fear their populations are falling to dangerous levels.

Above right: Walrus are killed for their tusks (above), which are used instead of elephant ivory.

**WILDSIDE WATCH**

**Arctic whales are at risk.**

- **Beluga or white whale: threatened by Eskimo hunting, and high levels of chemical pollutants in its body.**
- **Narwhal: hunted by Eskimos for its tusks.**
- **Bowhead: hunted by Eskimos. They kill fewer than 50 a year but even this could cause whale numbers to decline.**

**What you can do:**

- **Never buy a product made out of ivory. Narwhal tusks are an alternative to elephant ivory, and any increase in demand for any kind of ivory could mean that more of these whales are hunted and killed.**

# The coldest restaurant on Earth

ANTARCTICA IS TWICE the size of Australia and is covered by ice sheets several kilometres thick. Although it looks like a vast white desert, the great southern oceans that flow constantly around the continent support a cornucopia of marine life: 120 species of fish, 80 species of seabirds, 6 species of seals and 15 species of whale and dolphin can be found there.

## Krill on the menu

KRILL ARE TINY shrimp-like creatures 8–60 mm (¼–2½ in) long. There are some 600,000 billion of them in the Antarctic seas, with a combined weight greater than that of the entire human population. In one way or another, the krill support almost all life in the southern oceans.

The abundance of krill is because the Antarctic is ideal for the growth of phytoplankton, which krill eat. They feed on these microscopic plants at the ice edge in vast swarms and, in their turn, whales, birds and seals come and feed on the krill. Some species are specially adapted to eat krill: crabeater seals, for example, have multi-lobed teeth to sieve krill from the water, rather like the baleen plates of whales like blues and humpbacks.

Adelie penguins feed almost exclusively on krill, and krill form almost 80 per cent of all the food Antarctic birds eat. Other species that don't eat krill are still dependent on them: killer whales eat crabeater seals, and sperm whales; emperor penguins dive deep to catch squid that have fed on krill.

**Right: Krill can live for six to seven years. They survive the Antarctic winters by grazing phytoplankton under the ice.**

**Food circle**
Krill is a major source of food for five species of whale, three of seal and 20 of fish, as well as for penguins and several other birds. There is almost no other place in the world where the incredible abundance of a single species feeds so many others.

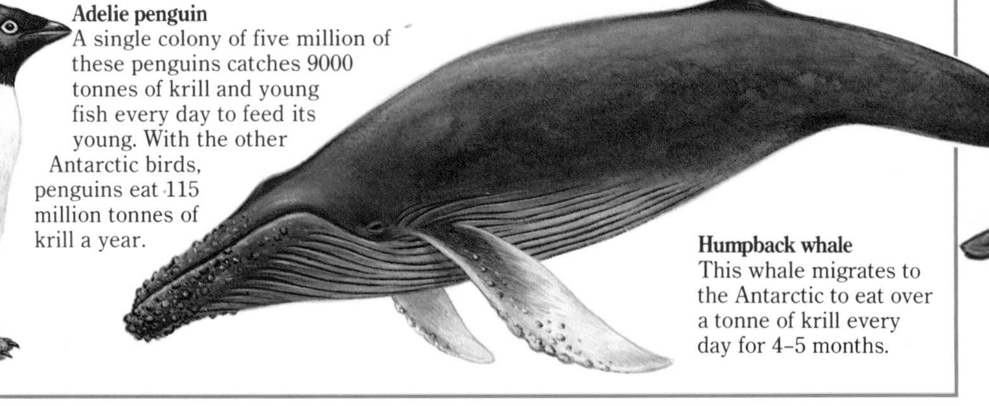

**Adelie penguin**
A single colony of five million of these penguins catches 9000 tonnes of krill and young fish every day to feed its young. With the other Antarctic birds, penguins eat 115 million tonnes of krill a year.

**Humpback whale**
This whale migrates to the Antarctic to eat over a tonne of krill every day for 4–5 months.

# Krill under threat?

HARVESTING KRILL has its problems. First, they go off soon after catching and contain dangerous levels of certain chemicals. Second, human foods made from krill are not popular: most of the half million tonnes taken every year is fed to animals.

Fishermen point out that, as whaling has reduced whale populations, there must be millions of tonnes of 'uneaten' krill available. In fact, populations of penguins and seals have grown and eat what the whales used to consume. Furthermore, no one knows how much krill fishermen could take without dangerously reducing the food available for Antarctic animals. Krill are also threatened by the hole in the ozone layer above the Antarctic. It lets in deadly ultra-violet light that can stop phytoplankton from growing.

If krill starve, so does the whole southern ocean.

**Large-scale commercial fishing of krill could remove the cornerstone of all life in the Antarctic Ocean.**

**WILDSIDE WATCH**

**There are threats to the Antarctic and also moves towards its protection.**

- **Tourism, mining and oil-drilling endanger breeding colonies on land and increase the risk of oil pollution in the sea.**
- **The Convention for the Conservation of Antarctic Living Marine Resources (CCALMR) aims to conserve all marine life in the southern oceans, and to prevent over-exploitation of any species.**
- **It has been suggested that the whole region could be made into a world park with exploitation of any kind banned.**

**What you can do:**

- **Write to your government representative and ask him or her to support the creation of an Antarctic world park.**

**Crabeater seal**
The world's most numerous seal, the crabeater breeds on the pack ice; its diet is 90 per cent krill. The crabeater is itself preyed on by the leopard seal.

# Captive killers

BECAUSE WHALES AND DOLPHINS have all the oceans in which to roam, we see them as symbols of freedom. Yet the number in captivity is growing. Zoos and aquaria worldwide, particularly in the United States, Europe and Japan now display them to eager onlookers.

Over 400 individual animals and 10 species are kept in the United States, but only one (the bottlenose dolphin) breeds successfully in captivity. This means that the oceans have to be raided time and again in order to add to the population in zoos and aquaria.

Performing whales and dolphins are big business: over 10 million people each year pay to see them at the American 'Sea World' complex. And the biggest and most spectacular of all the attractions is the killer whale.

## Co-operative success

KILLER WHALES ARE, in fact, dolphins – the biggest and fastest members of a family that is found throughout the world's oceans. They live in family groups called pods, comprising of between four and 40 individuals that stay together for life.

Pods hunt co-operatively and eat everything from squid to seals, even other whales such as blues. They communicate with each other using a complex pattern of clicks and squeaks that differ from pod to pod. The closeness of whale society is also revealed by the way they rear their young: females have a calf every eight years or so and keep it with them for several years after weaning. When captured, orcas are taken from their pod, the key to their survival and well-being.

**Right: The key to orca well-being is the pod, the tightly knit family group in which the whale spends its whole life.**

# Living – and dying – space

ONCE THOUGHT OF with fear, killer whales are now regarded with affection as well as curiosity. As a result of that curiosity, hundreds of orcas, as the whales are also known, have been taken from the oceans around Canada, Iceland and Alaska to end up in aquaria all over the world. The first one was displayed in Seattle in 1965. Many of these early captives died within five years, although they were young. In the wild, orcas survive for 50 to 100 years; they live in family groups and range over huge areas.

Some captured animals live in isolation, or in cramped pools. Others are kept in the best conditions with other orcas. Some of these have survived for many years and calves have been born although, by 1990, none had been successfully reared. Training and performing for the public provide some of the exercise and stimulation they would get in the wild from hunting their prey, and may make captivity more bearable.

**Left: Killer whales, or orcas, are not rare. However, many have been taken from the wild and, as a result, local populations have been reduced and the family structure of social groups has been destroyed.**

# The size of captivity

THERE ARE INTERNATIONAL agreements and national rules that govern how whales and dolphins should be kept in captivity.

However, the standards set for caring for killer whales vary greatly from country to country. A scientific study of orcas, kept in the best conditions to date, recommended a minimum pool size for a pod of five. Some pools do not come up to this standard.

**Pool size**
These are the minimum measurements, recommended by scientists, for keeping a pod of five killer whales.

Minimum volume
20,000 cu.m
(706,000 cu.ft);
should be doubled as soon as possible

Minimum depth
7.5 m (25 ft);
much of the pool should be
15 m (50 ft) deep

Minimum width
15 m (50 ft)

## WILDSIDE WATCH

**Many people disapprove of keeping killer whales and dolphins in captivity. But a great many of these animals *are* in dolphinaria and it is important that they are kept in the best possible conditions.**

- **Write to dolphinaria in your country and ask them about the conditions in which their captive killer whales and dolphins live.**
- **If animals have died or failed to breed in dolphinaria near you, write to the managers and ask: 'Why?' Write to your local newspaper about it.**
- **If you disapprove of keeping these animals in captivity, don't visit dolphinaria, and encourage other people to boycott them. If you do this, fewer killer whales and dolphins may be caught in the future.**

# A terrible slaughter

MOST OF US will never see a live whale, but 500 years ago you could stand on almost any sea cliff and see whales swimming by. Around the world they were a rich resource for people living on coasts. A single whale could feed a whole village and the oil from the layer of fat or blubber around its body was used to light lamps and fuel fires. These communities killed only as many animals as they needed to survive, and did not endanger whale populations.

Whales began to disappear when people hunted them for the profit they could make on their oil, whalebone or baleen, and meat.

## People of the whale

THE ESKIMOS, or Inuits, of northern Alaska call themselves 'the people of the whale'. For over 200 years they hunted the bowheads that migrate along the Alaskan coast. Using skin-covered boats and bone harpoons they killed the animals and dragged them back to shore. Each whale was shared amongst the community. Its every part had a use, nothing was wasted. The number of bowheads killed was so small it had no effect on the size of their population.

That way of life ended in the nineteenth century when commercial whalers almost wiped out the Alaskan bowheads. Today, the whale hunt is still central to Eskimo culture, but the hunters have paid jobs, live in houses and use modern boats and weapons to catch their prey.

**The Inuits' hunting methods never threatened the survival of the whale species they killed. Few animals were taken, and every part was used.**

## Whaling for profit

FROM THE TENTH CENTURY, the Basque people of northern Spain and south-west France used small boats and hand-held harpoons to kill right whales in the bay of Biscay, off the Spanish and French coasts. They sold oil from the animals' fat for lighting. By the end of the sixteenth century few of the species were left. Their population never recovered and today there are no right whales in the bay.

Throughout the seventeenth century, fleets of ships from Holland and England killed right whales and bowheads in the north Atlantic. The animals were caught at sea and butchered on the shore. Oil for lighting, and baleen or whalebone for everything from women's corsets to umbrella frames, were taken home at the end of the expedition. One population of whales after another was exterminated. By the beginning of the nineteenth century, it was not worth hunting the few animals that were left. Today, there are only a few hundred right whales and a few dozen bowheads in the north Atlantic.

**By the sixteenth century, commercial whaling had wiped out several populations of whales off the European coast.**

**Past prey**

**Bowhead whale:** 15–20 m (50–65 ft)
Its name comes from its bow-shaped jaw with huge baleen plates. The bowhead feeds close to the shore and ice edges in Arctic seas. It is rare, but protected except in Alaska where Eskimos are allowed to kill a few each year.

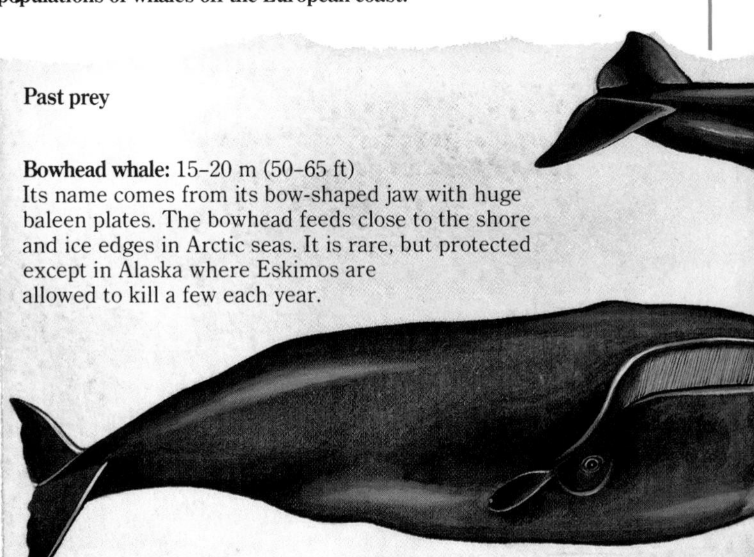

# Yankee whalers

By 1730, the Americans had killed most of the right whales along their east coast. To keep their successful whaling business going they turned to sperm whales. The oil of this species was better than any other and, by 1770, ships were sailing to Africa and South America in search of them.

Business boomed until 1860 and Yankee whalers roamed the Atlantic and Pacific oceans. Sperm whales were their main prey but they also hunted untouched populations of right whales. It was hard and dangerous work. The ships were powered by sail and whales were pursued in small rowing-boats and speared with hand-held harpoons. Voyages could last three or more years, a way of life recorded in Herman Melville's *Moby Dick*.

Whale oil, particularly high-quality sperm oil, was used in paint, margarine and cosmetics as well as for lighting. But by the 1880s, American whaling was dying, killed by competition from the new petroleum oil and the disruption to commerce caused by the Civil War 20 years earlier.

**Harpooning whales from small boats was dangerous, but nineteenth-century American whalers were instrumental in reducing sperm whale numbers.**

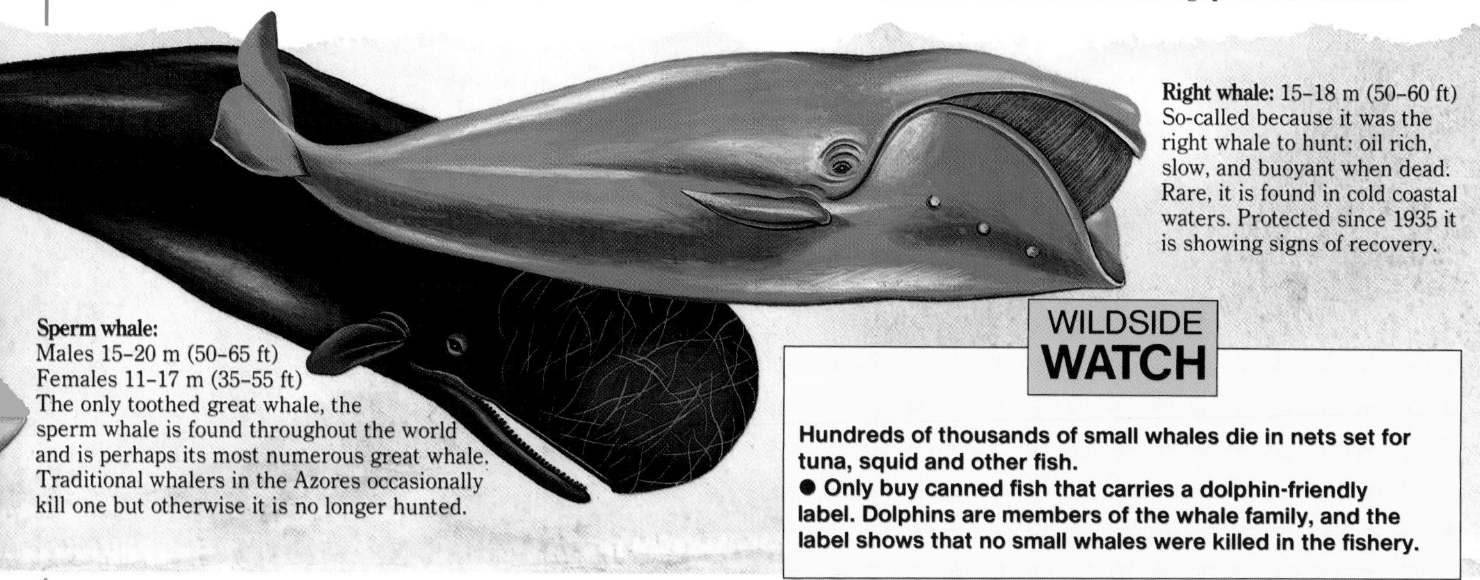

**Right whale:** 15–18 m (50–60 ft)
So-called because it was the right whale to hunt: oil rich, slow, and buoyant when dead. Rare, it is found in cold coastal waters. Protected since 1935 it is showing signs of recovery.

**Sperm whale:**
Males 15–20 m (50–65 ft)
Females 11–17 m (35–55 ft)
The only toothed great whale, the sperm whale is found throughout the world and is perhaps its most numerous great whale. Traditional whalers in the Azores occasionally kill one but otherwise it is no longer hunted.

WILDSIDE
**WATCH**

**Hundreds of thousands of small whales die in nets set for tuna, squid and other fish.**

**● Only buy canned fish that carries a dolphin-friendly label. Dolphins are members of the whale family, and the label shows that no small whales were killed in the fishery.**

# The killing goes on

AT THE END OF the nineteenth century, profits could still be made from whaling. But whalers were running out of whales to kill. Species like the blue, humpback, fin and sei were still plentiful because they had not been hunted. But they were fast swimming, deep diving and were found far from land. Two inventions sounded their death knell before the turn of the century: the metal-hulled steamship, which could move fast independently of the wind; and the harpoon gun, which shot an explosive charge into the whale's body from the deck of a large boat. The charge went off inside the animal and killed it before it could drag the boat.

## Whalers' boom, whales bust

STEAMSHIPS could penetrate Antarctic sea ice and the harpoon gun could bring down even a blue whale. The Norwegians, who invented the weapon, soon put it to use and exploited the untouched stocks of whales in the Antarctic. By 1911, 20,000 animals were being killed every year. At first, catcher ships brought dead whales ashore for butchering. Later, the Norwegians began to use huge factory ships to process them at sea. These saved time, so even more whales were killed. In 1931, the catch peaked at 55,000 animals. Other countries joined the killing: Britain, Japan, Germany, the United States, the USSR and Australia. The whalers initially took blue whales up to 30 m (100 ft) long. By 1938, these were running out and they turned to the next-biggest species, the fins. In the 1960s, the sei whales were their prey and finally, in the 1970s, the tiny minke, just 8 m (26 ft) long.

As whale populations fell, and substitutes were found for the oil, whaling became unprofitable. By the 1970s, only a few countries were in business.

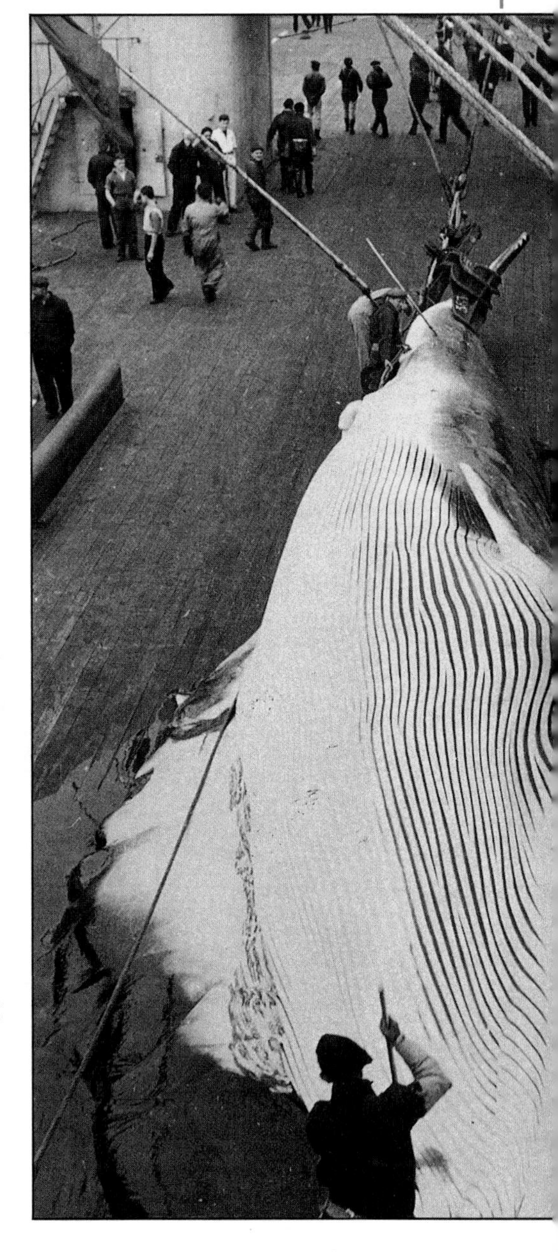

**Right: Factory ships speeded the destruction of whales in the Antarctic by processing even whole blue whales while still at sea.**

**Big whale, small whale**

**Blue whale:** 25–31 m (80–103 ft)
The largest animal that has ever lived, the blue whale is found worldwide but is dependent on polar feeding grounds. Its populations have never recovered from the large numbers that were killed in the 1930s. A survey in 1989 suggests numbers are dangerously low, despite total protection since 1966.

# Saving the whale?

In 1946, whaling countries formed the International Whaling Commission to try and control the killing of whales. But the IWC had no means of enforcing its quotas, which were constantly ignored. In the 1970s, environmental groups began to campaign to stop whaling, telling the public what beautiful and intelligent creatures whales were. In 1972, the United Nations called for a 10-year ban on all commercial whaling. Non-whaling countries, many of whom had by then joined the IWC, tried to persuade whaling nations to give up the practice. Finally, in 1982, the Commission voted to ban whaling until 1990. The ban was extended indefinitely in 1986.

Japan, Norway, Iceland and South Korea continue to kill whales. They avoid the IWC ban by claiming that they do so for 'scientific purposes'. The whales end up as meals in Japan, where their meat is considered a great delicacy and fetches a high price. Compared with the slaughter that has gone before, the numbers taken today are small.

**In 1986, years of campaigning and demonstrating finally brought a ban on whaling. But the practice still goes on and whales face new threats from pollution and overfishing.**

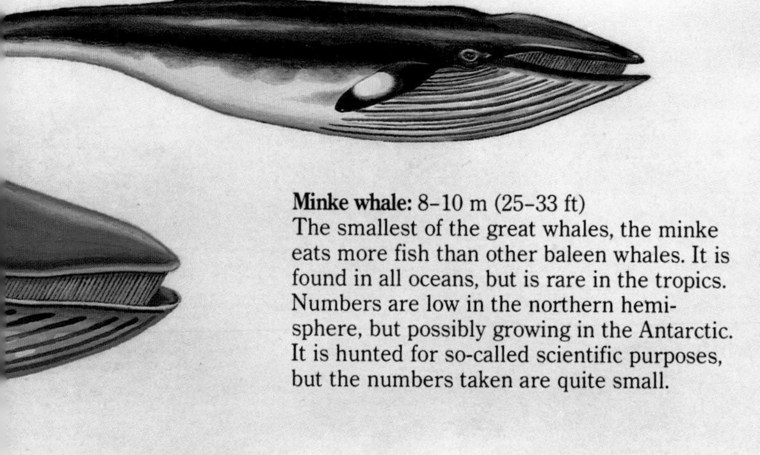

**Minke whale:** 8–10 m (25–33 ft)
The smallest of the great whales, the minke eats more fish than other baleen whales. It is found in all oceans, but is rare in the tropics. Numbers are low in the northern hemisphere, but possibly growing in the Antarctic. It is hunted for so-called scientific purposes, but the numbers taken are quite small.

There are 10 species of great whale. All, with the exception of the sperm whale, are baleen whales which have comb-like baleen plates, instead of teeth, to sieve food from the sea.
Blue whale
Fin whale
Sei whale
Minke whale
Brydes whale
Humpbacked whale
Grey whale
Right whale
Sperm whale
Bowhead whale

## WILDSIDE WATCH

**Whales are recovering from the years when they were hunted, but populations may never regain pre-whaling levels.**
- **Never buy whale meat or other whale products.**
- **Join an organisation that campaigns for whale conservation.**
- **If your country has not banned whale-hunting, write to your government to protest about it.**

# Save our seas!

THE PROBLEMS that face Planet Ocean and its wildlife are enormous, and growing every day. It's easy to feel helpless when we are faced with pollution, overfishing and habitat destruction on a huge worldwide scale; easy to feel that it is all happening far away and that there is nothing we can do about it.

But a great deal is occurring very close to home – and you can help to stop it by keeping your eyes open, and telling people what you see and find out.

Where does the waste-water and sewage from your house go? Is it emptied into your local river, which flows to the sea? Is it dumped directly on to a beach? Are there factories near where you live? What happens to their waste: does it go into a river or the sea? When you visit the seaside, do you see fish and birds? How many? Are there more or less than when you came before? Is the sea more polluted?

Ask your friends, teachers and parents to help keep an eye on what is happening to your river, to your sea shore. Tell your local newspaper, radio and television station what you find. Talk to your government representative. Your ACTION can help to Save Our Seas!

Above: Hundreds of terns, wintering on the coast of Ghana in West Africa, used to die when children trapped them. Then the Royal Society for the Protection of Birds (RSPB), the International Council for Bird Preservation (ICBP) and the Ghanaian government started wildlife clubs for the children - who now help to count terns and tell people about conservation.

Left: When children from a Dutch coastal village found that their beach was to be used as a dump for toxic waste, which would be covered with soil and rocks and then built on, they campaigned against the plan on television and radio and through the press until it was dropped.

Below: Young people from 10 European countries took part in Coastwatch surveys in September 1989 and 1990. From Iceland in the north to Portugal in the south, 5-km (3-mile) blocks of coastline were surveyed for pollution and damage. The results are reported to the European Commission, Brussels.

# Useful addresses

**By using your eyes, ears and brain, you can find out lots about the sea, and help to protect it. Add your efforts to those of others by joining one or more of these organisations. It is a good idea to enclose a stamped, self-addressed envelope when you write asking for information.**

**The Marine Conservation Society**
9 Gloucester Road
Ross-on-Wye
Herefordshire
HR9 5BU
*Campaigns for the conservation of marine habitats in Britain and around the world. Runs projects studying, and campaigning for, marine species.*

**Greenpeace**
30–31 Islington Green
London
N1 8XE
*Campaigns for the conservation of the world's oceans. Particularly active on marine pollution, driftnetting, the greenhouse effect and the Antarctic.*

**Whale and Dolphin Conservation Society**
19a James Street West
Bath
BA1 2BT
*Works for the conservation of whales and dolphins worldwide. Campaigns for an end to all whaling and dolphin deaths in nets.*

**World Wide Fund for Nature**
Panda House
Weyside Park
Catteshall Road
Godalming
Surrey
GU7 1XR
*Runs research and conservation projects all over the world. Many aim to conserve marine species and habitats.*

**Wildfowl and Wetlands Trust**
Slimbridge
Gloucestershire
GL2 7BT
*Works to conserve waterfowl and their habitats through research, education and campaigning.*

**WATCH Clubs**
c/o Royal Society for Nature Conservation (RSNC)
The Green
Witham Park
Waterside South
Lincoln LN5 7JR
*Young people's group that campaigns to protect wildlife of all kinds.*

# Index

**Africa** 27, 29, 34, 43, 62–3
Alaska 10–11, 25, 27, 53, 58
Albatrosses 24
Algae 30, 36, 37
Alien (introduced) species 25, 40–1
Anchovetta 44
Antarctic Ocean 8, 9, 54–5, 60
Aquaria 38, 56–7
Arctic Ocean 52–3
Atlantic Ocean 33, 43, 49, 58–9
Auks 13
Australia 36, 39, 43, 54

**Barnacles** 14, 15, 32, 33
Beaches 14–19
Birds 5, 7, 8–9, 10, 12–13, 17, 19, 20, 21, 23, 24–5, 29, 32, 35, 40, 54, 63
Boats 20, 30, 31
Breeding 13, 14, 17, 18, 24, 25, 28, 35, 42–3
Building materials 17, 39

**Canada** 27, 45, 53
Captivity 38, 39, 41, 56–7
Chemical pollution 8, 14, 22–3, 33, 34, 43, 53
Climate 4, 33, 38, 52
Coastal waters 5, 7, 8, 14–19, 30, 32, 53
Cockles 17
Cod 45
Conservation 62–3; *see also* Wildlife Watch boxes on 4, 7, 9, 10, 13, 14 and all odd-numbered pages thereafter
Coral atolls and reefs 4, 7, 10, 28, 30, 32, 36–7, 40
Cosmetics 49
Crabs 16–17, 28–9, 32–3
Cuckoos, mangrove 29
Curlews 21
Currents 6, 7, 32–3, 42–3, 44
Cuttlefish 30

**Dams** 42
Darwin, Charles 41
Deep sea 50–1
Dogfish 27
Dolphins 23, 42, 44, 46–7, 56–7, 63
killer whales (a type of dolphin) 4, 10, 42, 56–7
Ducks 19, 21

**Eagles** 12–13
Elephants 48, 53
Endangered species 24, 30, 34–5, 41, 49
Endemic species 40–1
Eskimos (Inuits) 58
Europe 16, 17, 22–3, 27, 34, 56
Evolution 40–1
*Exxon Valdez* 10, 12–13

**Feather stars** 4
Fish 9, 13, 20, 23, 25, 27, 28, 29, 30, 32, 35, 36, 42–3, 45, 46–7, 52, 59
Fishing industry 4, 5, 16, 25, 26–7, 30, 31, 33, 34, 41–7, 54–5, 62
Food chains and webs 5, 8–9, 22–3, 32, 46, 52
Fossil fuels 33
Fur trade 26

**Gannets** 7, 32
Geese 21, 31
Greenhouse effect 33, 38, 52
Guillemots 5
Gulls 35, 42

**Habitats** 6–7, 24, 62, 63
Heavy metals 22–3, 34
Herons 29
Herrings 32

**Indian Ocean** 25
Industrial pollution 5, 8–9, 14, 21, 30, 34–5, 62
Irish Sea 8
Islands 40–1
Ivory 53

**Jellyfish** 32
Jewellery 5

**Killer whales** (a type of dolphin) 4, 10, 42, 56
Krill 54–5

**Lichens** 15
Limestone 36–9
Limpets 14, 15
Litter 17, 23
Lobsters 27, 28, 32, 43

**Mangrove swamps** 28–9
Marram grass 19
Medicines 5, 29
Mediterranean sea 34–5
Migration 10, 17, 21, 25, 42
Mineral mining 5, 25, 30, 51–2, 55
Mud 20–1, 28
Murrelets 25
Mussels 14

**Nesting** 24–5
Nets 46–7
Nitrogen 32
North America 17
North Sea 22–3, 43
Nuclear waste 8, 22–3, 51, 62–3
Nutrients 6, 7, 8, 10, 20, 28, 32, 36–7, 38, 51, 62–3

**Octopuses** 27
Oil pollution 4, 5, 10–13, 14, 20–1, 25, 27, 30, 34–5, 52, 55
Overfishing 4, 5, 27, 34, 43
Oxygen 8, 10, 16, 21, 23, 28, 30, 33, 50
Ozone layer 55

**Pacific Ocean** 27, 39, 41, 42, 46
Penguins 8–9, 24, 54–5
Plankton 7, 10, 13, 17, 22–3, 32, 33, 43, 49, 52, 54
Plastic rubbish 9, 23
Polar bears 52
Polar habitats 7, 10, 14, 32, 33, 43, 49, 52, 58–9
Pollination 28
Pollution 4–5, 8–9, 10–13, 14, 20–3, 33, 34, 41, 43, 51, 52–3, 62–3
Porpoises 10, 23
Prawns 28, 29, 30
Puffins 10, 12, 13, 32, 44

**Rivers** 8, 20–1, 42, 62
Rocky shores 14–15, 26, 43, 46, 53
Roots, mangrove 28

**Salmon** 25, 42–3, 46
Saltmarshes 20–1
Sandy beaches 16–19, 30–1, 43
Sand eels 44
Sanderlings 17
Sea bed 5, 7, 39, 46, 51
Sea-birds 5, 7, 9, 10, 24–5, 32, 35, 42, 56, 53
Sea cows 30–1
Sea grasses 30–1
Sea levels 38
Sea lions 10, 12, 41, 42
Seals 12, 20, 22–3, 27, 32, 34–5, 42, 52, 54–5, 56
Sea otters 10, 12, 26–7
Seashores 14–19
Sea urchins 26–7, 28
Seaweed 7, 8, 12, 14, 15, 20, 26–7, 32, 36, 43
Sewage 5, 8–9, 14, 16–17, 21, 22–3, 33–4, 38, 41, 51, 62–3
Shallow waters 46
Sharks 41, 48–9
Shellfish 14, 20, 26, 46, 53
Shrimps 30, 36
Silt 30–1, 38–9
Snails 21, 28, 30
Snakes 40–1
South America 44
South-East Asia 29
Spawning 14, 28, 42–3, 45
Sponges 15
Squid 30, 32, 46, 50–1, 54, 56, 59
Starfish 14, 16, 39

**Teal** 21
Temperate seas 32
Terns 32, 63
Terrapins 29
Threats to oceans *see* fishing industry; greenhouse effect; pollution; tourism; whaling industry
Tides 14, 20, 26, 31
Tortoises 41
Tourism 16–19, 20, 23, 29, 33–4, 39, 41, 55
Trade 26, 39, 53
Trees 28–9, 39, 40, 41, 43
Tropical habitats 7, 14, 17, 28–9, 30, 47
Tuna 46–7, 59
Turtles 18–19, 30, 41, 46–7

**USA** 26, 27, 56–7

**Volcanoes** 40, 41

**Walruses** 53
Waves 14, 36
Whales 10, 12, 19, 32, 45, 46, 50–1, 53, 56–61, 62, 63
Whaling industry 58–61, 62, 63
Whelks 14, 15
Worms 16, 20–1, 32, 46, 51

**Zoos** 56–7

**Picture credits** (key: l – left, r – right, t – top, c – centre, b – bottom, tl – top left, tr – top right, bl – bottom left, br – bottom right)
**Allstock** pages 10–11 (J. Schultz); **Ardea** pages 4 (t, F. Gohier; b, P. Morris), 13 (tl, L. & T. Bomford), 31 (b, R. & V. Taylor), 36 (tr, R. & V. Taylor), 38 (b, R. & V. Taylor), 41, 48 (l, R. & V. Taylor), 53 (t, P. Morris) and 56 (b, F. Gohier); **Bridgeman Art Library/Private Collection** ('The Whale Fishery – Laying On', 1862, by Currier & Ives) page 59; **British Antarctic Survey** page 55 (I. Everson); **Kostas Christou** page 35 (l); **Bruce Coleman** pages 26–7 (J. Foott), 30 (b, F. Lanting), 31 (r, G. Langsbury), 35 (r, J. Grande), 52–3 (b, E. & P. Bauer) and 54–5 (I. Everson); **Delaware State Archives** page 17 (l); **DRK Photo** page 25 (bl, J. Foott); **Environmental Picture Library** pages 5 (t, S. Gamester) and 16 (V. Miles); **Mary Evans Picture Library** page 49 (t); **Explorer** page 13 (br, P. Cheuva); **Jeff Foott** page 26 (b); **Jennifer Fry** page 61; **Genesis Space Photo Library** page 6; **Greenpeace** pages 12 (tl, Merjenburgh), 46 (l & r, Grace), 47 (Morgan) and 51 (t, Morgan); **Robert Harding** pages 5 (cr, L. Tettora), 17 (r), 24 (r) and 25 (t, P. van Riel); **Hollandse Hoogte** page 62 (E. de Kam); **Eric & David Hosking** pages 33 (tl & bl, D. P. Wilson) and 52–3 (t); **Hulton-Deutsch Collection** page 58 (t); **Jacana** page 34 (b); **Frank Lane** page 7 (tr, S. Jonasson), 19 (r, R. Tidman), 22–3 (R. Tidman), 23 (R. Tidman), 44 (l, T. Wharton), 45 (r, D. Robinson) and 56–7 (R. van Nostrand); **Magnum** pages 12–13 (P. Fusco) and 13 (tr, J. Gaumy); **Mansell Collection** page 24 (l); **Nature Photographers** page 18 (l); **NHPA** pages 5 (b, K. Ghani), 30–1 (ANT/D. Parer), 36 (br, A. Bannister), 49 (b, ANT/K. Aitken) and 53 (b, S. Krasemann)); **Norwich Union Coastwatch UK** page 63 (t); **Oxford Scientific Films** page 4 (cl, D. Lee), 7 (tl, Animals Animals/L. Trusty), 25 (br, D. Allan), 37 (t, L. Gould; b, S. Cunliffe), 38 (t, M. Gibbs), 43 (t, P. Parks; b, Animals Animals/L. L. Rue) and 50 (P. Parks); **Photo Researchers** page 45 (l, W. R. Curtsinger); **Planet Earth** pages 4 (cr, C. Roessler), 5 (cl, J. Duncan), 7 (b, R. Arnold), 14 (J. Bracegirdle), 18–19 (F. Schulke), 34, 36 (l, P. Atkinson), 39 (bl, R. Salm; br, W. Williams), 48 (r, J. Wall) and 51 (b, R. Hessler); **RSPB** page 63 (b, C. Gomersall); **Smithsonian Institution, Washington** page 58 (b); **Survival Anglia** pages 12 (tr, J. Foott), 29 (F. Koster), 33 (r, M. Price), 39 (t, J. Foott) and 53 (c, J. Foott); **Town Docks Museum, Kingston upon Hull** page 60–1; **Koen van Waerebeek** page 44 (r).
**Illustrators** Graham Allen, Stephen Lings, Mick Loates, Shane Marsh, Jane Pickering, Richard Smith, (Linden Artists). Kuo Kang Chen, Selwyn Hutchinson, Richard Phipps.